Contents

1 04671 5 Copyright © 1980 Purnell & Sons Ltd., Published 1980 by Purnell Books, Berkshire House, Queen Street, Maidenhead, Berkshire
Made and printed in Great Britain by Purnell & Sons Ltd., Paulton (Bristol) and London

The Girl Guide Annual 1981

Published by special arrangement with
THE GIRL GUIDES ASSOCIATION

Purnell

Escape to Freedom

Gail, Patrol Leader of the Herons, glanced at the assembled girls in the Guide headquarters, and frowned. There were two missing from the Heron Patrol. Suzanne was away on holiday with her parents, but where was Fiona?

Fiona was the new Second of the Herons. She was untried, but promised well, as she was keen, although rather shy. Her selection by Gail had been something of a surprise and it had rather upset Stephanie, who was much more outgoing and had really expected to be chosen.

Fiona lived in a country village several miles away, but this didn't stop her from being regular at Guide meetings, to which she cycled in all weathers.

Robbie held up her arms for silence and then gave the hand signal to indicate, "Fall in—in Patrols."

One advantage of having Mrs Roberts—affectionately called Robbie—as a Guider was that she was free to organise weekday activities during the long summer holidays.

"Right, girls! Has everybody brought haversack rations for the day? Good! Then this is it. Today we are living in an occupied country where Guiding has been declared illegal. The Herons have been caught holding Patrol meetings and imprisoned in this hall. They have planned an escape. The rest of you are occupying forces and will do all you can to stop them from reaching the border and the safety of the adjoining country."

"They won't even get out of this hall, Robbie," Emma of the Robins called out, grinning.

"Oh, yes, you must let them go—just for the fun of catching them again—if you can! I'll give the Herons this map, on which I have marked the border between us and the West. Fiona hasn't turned up yet, I see, Gail, so you'll have to leave without her unless she comes soon. The first town over the border is Westborough. If the Herons reach the market-place there by four o'clock this afternoon they will have escaped."

"But, Westborough is ten miles away!" cried Christine.

Robbie laughed. "Yes! Use any means you like to get there. It's a test of your ingenuity. We shall be watching the bus routes. The use of parents' cars is banned."

"How do we get captured?" asked Fleur.

"As long as you can be identified and your name called out, you are caught. You have come in activity dress, as I asked, but your pursuers will be in uniform, so you'll have a chance of spotting them before they spot you."

"If one gets captured, can the others still escape?" asked Stephanie.

Robbie nodded. "I see you have already entered into the spirit of the game, Stephanie. Whoever is captured won't be required to tell of the whereabouts of the others, who will be free to go on, so that if one of you is caught the remainder can still get through."

No further questions were asked. Robbie waited a little longer for Fiona to arrive, but then gave the word to start. "The Herons will stay here," she said. "Everybody else will leave. To give the Herons a fair chance of getting clear, we won't watch the hall. We'll give you ten minutes to break away, Gail. After that, any sighting means you're recaptured. Captured or free, we meet in the market-place at Westborough at four o'clock. I'll tell Fiona you've gone if she arrives. She must join the hunters. Right! Off we go!"

"Any ideas, Gail?" the P.L. was asked when the Herons were left alone. Gail smoothed out the map on a table. "Fiona is a jolly good map-reader. She's won the badge. I'm not as expert, but as she's not here I'll do my best. Here's Hampton; that's us. Robbie's marked the border between us and freedom. Here's Westborough, just over the border. Which direction is that?"

"North-east," replied Stephanie promptly. "I fancy I can read a map as well as Fiona."

"Maybe you'll need to prove it presently," said Gail dryly. "Anyway, let's go now. There's a bus stop opposite the hall, and a bus is due."

"What's the plan?" Joanne

asked when the six Guides had climbed to the upper deck of a south-bound bus.

"At the moment it's only vague, but I thought we'd stand a chance of escaping by going to the outskirts of Hampton and then catching buses connecting villages, then find a way of sneaking into Westborough."

"We'd better keep our eyes open for Guide uniforms," said Stephanie. "Duck if you see one."

"Duck!" cried Marie a moment later.

Everyone crouched down in her seat, except Marie. She laughed.

"Sorry, girls! My mistake. It was a woman wearing a blue jumper."

"Was that supposed to be a joke?" asked Stephanie, rather crossly.

"Sorry!" muttered Marie, looking rather abashed at Stephanie's tone. "I really did think it was a Guide."

The bus crossed the bridge over the river that led to the outer suburbs of Hampton. Gail jumped up.

"Next stop, girls!" she said, and clattered down the stairs.

"What's the idea, Gail?" asked Christine, as the Patrol returned to the centre of the bridge.

"Something I saw as we passed by," Gail told her. She pointed to a small cabin-cruiser moored at the side of the river. A figure in jeans and sweater was moving about on board.

"You're not thinking of commandeering it to escape in, are you?" asked Fleur.

"There's no need to," replied Gail. "That's *Water Nymph.* It belongs to my Uncle John. He usually keeps her down-river at the Shellingford Marina, but my cousin, Sam, is evidently using it."

By the time the Guides reached the moored craft its occupant had disappeared into the cabin.

"Ahoy there, Sam!"

A head and shoulders appeared in the cabin entrance. To their surprise, the Herons saw that it was a girl.

"Meet the Herons!" said Gail. "Herons, this is my cousin, Samantha. May we come aboard, Sam?"

"You're welcome!" said Sam.

"Into the cabin and keep out of sight," ordered Gail.

"*Water Nymph* is due in for an engine check," explained Sam. "I'm taking her to the marina now. Then I'm going on to take part in the gymkhana at Fortfield."

"The marina is halfway to Westborough," Gail pointed out to the others triumphantly. "Sam, by the way, has two passions in life, boats and horses." She explained to Sam that they were trying to escape over the border to freedom, and Sam readily agreed to take them as far as the marina.

As the cruiser chugged down the river, the Guides kept a sharp lookout. They saw nothing more ominous than a few anglers and a live example of their Patrol bird—also fishing.

At the marina, they thanked Sam. Then Gail, who had been studying the map with Stephanie, led the way to a disused railway running parallel with the river. They all scrambled down the overgrown embankment to the track. All the lines and sleepers had gone, but the weed-grown flint ballast remained.

"This continues until it joins the main line at Westborough," Gail told them. "The embankments will give us cover all the way; but keep alert. The first one to spot any sign that we have been sighted, signal. Then all take cover."

The Patrol tramped on in single file for a considerable dis-

She pointed to a small cabin cruiser moored on the river . . .

tance. They were congratulating themselves that they had got clear of likely pursuit when Stephanie, who was leading, gave a sudden signal. The six froze, then doubled into any cover that was near. Three dived beneath a stunted elder-tree, two crouched behind a clump of brambles. Gail landed uncomfortably in a bed of nettles. From there, she made her way cautiously to the elder-tree.

"What did you see, Stephanie?" she whispered.

"I saw Fiona," was the surprising reply.

"You saw who?"

"Fiona."

"Fiona? You must be mistaken."

Stephanie shrugged. "Take a peep yourself."

"I'll do that."

Very cautiously, Gail peeped over the top of the embankment. After taking a long look, she returned. Her expression was puzzled.

"Yes, it's Fiona all right. I can't understand what she's doing right out here. She surely can't have gone to the hall and then got to here. I dare say she got to the hall late, and she may have joined the others in hunting, but she isn't on her bike."

"Shall I tell you what I think?" asked Stephanie. "I think our new Second decided to go to the gymkhana instead of to Guides. You know she's mad on horses, and I suppose the gymkhana at Fortfield is a great attraction to her."

"I don't believe that," said Gail. "She told me she was looking forward to this wide game."

"Perhaps she was on her way to the Guide hall and just dropped in at the gymkhana," suggested Christine.

"It's a funny way to get to the Guide hall, via Fortfield—about eight miles off the route," said Stephanie, a touch of asperity in her voice.

"It's not so far on a bike," said Gail.

"It's the kind of thing that happens to horsy people," put in Fleur. "They can't resist the sound of the hunt or the gymkhana or whatever."

Gail frowned. "Well, for our own safety, we must treat her as one of the hunters," she stated. "Don't let her see us."

Gail was at a loss to explain the unexpected appearance of Fiona. She knew that what Stephanie had said about Fiona's love of horses was true. Fiona's parents were not that well off and Fiona had little chance of riding, but she was very knowledgeable about horses, and her greatest ambition was to own a pony of her own. Stephanie's parents were very well off, and Stephanie had recently been given a pony of her own. She had not yet invited Fiona to ride it, and Fiona would never ask for the privilege, but Gail had thought how ironic it was that Stephanie, who had no real interest in horses, should own a pony while Fiona, a genuine horse-lover, had hardly any opportunity of riding, let alone owning, one.

The Guides waited for a time, but there was no further sighting of Fiona or of a Guide uniform, so Gail gave the word to move on.

At the end of half an hour she called a halt.

"Time for sandwiches," she announced.

"And not a moment too soon," said Marie. "Another five minutes and you'd have had a collapsed escapee on your hands."

Fleur sank thankfully down

where she was and opened her haversack.

"Not there, you nit!" Gail admonished her. "Anybody coming along the track would see you at once. Let's all get down where we can see without being seen."

The Herons ate their food under the cover of large clumps of gorse. "How far are we from freedom now?" asked Joanne through a mouthful of egg sandwich.

Gail spread out the map. "If we continue along the railway for two and a half miles until we reach the junction we shall be about a mile from the border at Westborough. We can shorten the distance by starting to cut across country now, but that will mean crossing the river. We shall be rather exposed."

"Let's carry on the way we're going," urged Joanne. "It's been safe so far."

"So far," agreed Gail, "but the hunters will be well spread out by now. The most dangerous leg of the journey faces us now."

Immediately there was a shout. "You're caught, Fleur!"

"Then let's show a leg!" said Marie.

"Yes, let's go!" cried Fleur, and jumped up impetuously.

Immediately there was a shout. "You're caught, Fleur!"

The Herons sank back in dismay behind the gorse-bush. The hunters were closer than any of them had imagined.

"We've underestimated them," muttered Gail.

"Put your hands on your head, Fleur, and walk towards me."

The Herons recognised the voice of Sarah, of the Swallow Patrol.

"Don't look down!" Gail hissed to Fleur. "Do as she says. Don't give 'em a hint that we're here too."

Through the bush, the Herons watched Fleur walk towards her captor. They all held their breath. Would Sarah come forward to investigate? To their great relief, they saw Sarah turn and urge Fleur in front of her along the track.

"Quick! While their backs are turned, race up the bank and over

the top. They're sure to come to see whether there are others with Fleur. I'll go first. If there's no challenge, follow me—double-quick!"

Gail ran. Nobody challenged. Sarah had evidently been alone when she saw Fleur. She would certainly tell the other hunters of her capture and bring them to the spot.

Above the embankment, the ground sloped up to a wood.

"What now?" asked Christine when the Patrol reached the shelter of the wood.

"Through the wood. We'll see what's on the other side."

"They'll be hot on our track now," said Marie.

"But it's exciting!" laughed Joanne.

Beyond the wood the ground was dotted with a number of coppices. Gail decided to run from wood to wood, making what use they could as cover of the folds of the ground in between. Some time later, to use Stephanie's phrase, they 'ran out of woods.'

"But there's only the river to cross now and then we'll be ready for the last dash in to Westborough," said Gail.

"The last dash, across the bridge into Westborough, will be the hardest part, though," said Christine, and the others agreed.

"We haven't done badly, though, so far," said Stephanie. "Only one capture."

"Fleur was jolly good," said Marie. "She didn't give us away by looking back or anything."

"She behaved like a true Heron," declared Christine.

"I can see the bridge from here," said Joanne, "and I can't see anybody on it."

"Which isn't surprising when you come to think about it," said Stephanie sarcastically. "Even

non-Herons wouldn't be idiots enough to show themselves waiting on the bridge."

"Are they watching it, though—that's the question," said Gail. "I'm inclined to think our best plan will be to make for the bridge as fast as we can in case they haven't yet had time to cover it. After all, we cut out a lot of miles by going down-river on *Water Nymph*."

Stephanie nodded. "I agree. Speed's the thing now."

"Don't forget that Sarah will soon get the message back that we're on this side of the river, and when she does that every crossing-point will be watched."

Nearing the bridge, the Herons hid behind a hedge and scrutinised the bridge for signs of watchers. There was no indication that anyone was on or near it. Gail came to a decision.

"Let's go," she said, adding, "one by one at short intervals. You first, Christine."

From the hedge, Christine ran along the track leading to the bridge. There was no challenge.

"Now you, Marie!" breathed Gail.

Marie followed swiftly after Christine.

"Now you, Joanne!"

There was no challenge. Gail and Stephanie looked triumphantly at each other. To win through with only the loss of Fleur would be a magnificent feat. Then their expressions changed to dismay. Two Guides suddenly broke cover with shouts of "Christine, Marie, Joanne! You're in the bag!"

From the hedge, the remaining two Herons watched despondently as the other three surrendered. The two Guides had been concealed in an old boat lying disused on the river-bank below the bridge, and they had let the

Herons get right up to the bridge before springing out and capturing them.

"The crafty so-and-so's," murmured Gail admiringly. "We've got to admit it was a neat capture, Stephanie."

Stephanie nodded gloomily. "We haven't much of a chance of getting across now without being spotted, and if we don't move soon they'll be coming to see whether there are any other Herons about to make a run for it."

"There is a chance, and it's coming along now," said Gail excitedly. She pointed through the hedge.

A van was rumbling slowly along the track towards the bridge. It was drawn by a big but evidently old horse, and it would pass almost within touch of the hidden Herons.

"The van is only moving at walking pace," Gail whispered to Stephanie. "If we nip out behind it and keep close behind it we won't be seen—or we might not be seen. When it reaches the bridge we'll move alongside it so that we'll be hidden by it from anyone lurking on the riverbank."

"It's worth trying."

"Get ready, then."

As the van passed by them, the girls could read the name lettered on the side of the van. It was J. JONES, SCRAP MERCHANT. They jumped swiftly through a gap in the hedge and then pressed themselves close against the tarpaulin draped down the back of it. They were out of sight of the driver, and, they hoped, of sharp Guide eyes. The tarpaulin flapped open as the van jogged up and down on the rough surface of the track, and the girls saw that it was filled with a miscellaneous jumble of scrap.

"How about getting inside?" whispered Stephanie.

"We ought not to do it without asking the driver," replied Gail, "but it's so full of junk, anyhow, that we'd have a job to find room! If we keep close—"

She stopped, cut short by a triumphant shout. "Gail, Stephanie, you're caught!"

Several Guides who had lain concealed behind the buttress of the bridge below the road rushed out.

"We saw your legs," laughed Margaret, P.L. of the Swallows.

"You might have got by if you'd been inside the van," commented Anne, Second of the Kingfishers.

"I told you we ought to have hidden inside the van," whispered Stephanie disgustedly.

"It's a hundred-per-cent recapture," grinned Audrey, one of the Robin Patrol.

"It's back to the cells for you!" grinned another Swallow.

"It's a fair cop," admitted Gail, and Stephanie nodded gloomily.

"By the way, your Second turned up in Westborough," Margaret told them.

"Fiona?"

"Yes."

"Was she hunting with you?"

"No. She's in some sort of trouble, we gather."

The Herons learned about Fiona when they were triumphantly escorted to Robbie and the rest of the Company waiting in Westborough market-place.

It appeared that Fiona had set off for the Guide hall, but had cycled first to the cottage of an old lady near Fortfield to take something from her mother. On coming out of the cottage, she found that her bike had gone. The cottage was in an isolated country lane, and someone had made off with it. Fiona had no idea who could have stolen it. She was stranded. Rather than worry the old lady with an account of her loss, she made her way to Westborough on foot to report the loss to the police there and to get the bus back to her home.

At Westborough the police had taken particulars of the bike, but hadn't held out a lot of hope of recovering it, as there had been a number of cycles stolen and tracing them was difficult. Fortunately, Fiona ran into Robbie in the market-place, and was able to join up with the Guides.

Fiona was upset. A bike was essential to her, as she lived a long distance from town and school and Guide hall.

"How about getting inside?" whispered Stephanie

"I'm sorry I couldn't get to Guides, Gail," she said to the P.L. "I was keen on taking part in the wide game, and I should have been there on time if my bike hadn't been stolen."

"And I was certain she'd gone to the gymkhana," Stephanie murmured to Gail contritely. "I feel a bit of a beast for thinking that. I'm sorry for Fiona."

"So you should be," said Gail bluntly. To Fiona she said, "If I remember rightly, your bike is blue, isn't it, Fiona?"

"That's it—Guide colour!" Fiona tried to smile.

"I may be wrong," said Gail, "but—come with me, Fiona. I'm going to have a word with Robbie. When we were trying to escape the eagle eyes of the Robins and Swallows and Kingfishers, we got behind a van. I could see inside. In fact, Stephanie had the bright idea of hiding inside. The van was full of junk of all kinds, but when I come to think about it, it wasn't all junk. There were a couple of bikes there. It struck me at the time, though I didn't give much thought to it, that they looked rather good to be in with the rest of the old scrap there. I'm wondering now—"

"You mean, you think one of the bikes might be mine?" cried Fiona excitedly.

Gail nodded. "I don't want to raise your hopes too much, but I'm going to tell Robbie of my suspicions."

When Gail told Robbie how she and Stephanie had kept behind the van to escape detection in crossing the bridge, and saw inside the van, Robbie said, "We'll go to the police-station at once and ask them to investigate the van. Should you know it again, Gail?"

Gail nodded emphatically. "It

. . . Fiona, I know you'd like to go in for the Horsewoman badge . . .

can't be far away, either," she added. "It's got a name on the side—J. Jones, Scrap Merchant."

Robbie wasted no time, but took Gail, Stephanie and Fiona to the local police-station. The sergeant in charge there showed immediate interest in what Gail told him.

"This may be the very lead we've been looking for for months," he stated. "There have been a lot of bikes stolen in this district, and we haven't been able to trace them. If this scrap merchant Jones has got this young lady's bike in his van we've got him. If it turns out that way we'll be most obliged to you for putting us in the way of catching him."

"We're going to have a cup of tea in the café in the market-place," Robbie told him. "Then we'll come back to see whether you've caught up with the van."

Fiona's dejection had given way to hope now. By the time all the Guides had had tea she was looking forward eagerly to hearing good news about her bike.

"I can hardly wait to finish tea," she whispered excitedly to Gail.

The first thing that met her eyes when Robbie led the Guides into the police-station were two bikes, one of which was in Guide blue.

"It's mine! Oh, I'm so thankful!" Fiona cried.

"So am I," said the sergeant, coming forward. "You can identify your bike? Good! We've caught our man with the loot on him, so to speak, so he can't get out of it. There's quite a chance we may get back from his scrapyard several of the other bikes he's stolen. He changes their appearance, though, so it mayn't be easy. Anyway, you've got yours back safely, young lady, and that's a relief. I must say," he added, turning to Robbie, "your Guides keep their wits about them."

"That's one of the things Guiding teaches girls to do," replied Robbie proudly.

"Well, even if all the Herons got captured," remarked Stephanie, as they walked back to the market-place, "they made a pretty good capture themselves, eh?"

"Thanks to Gail," said Robbie.

"And Stephanie," put in Gail generously.

"Thank you, Gail," said Fiona gratefully. "Thank you, Stephanie."

"It was Gail's sharp eyes that did it," said Stephanie. "By the way, Fiona, I know you'd like to go in for the Horsewoman badge. Well, if you'd like to practise whatever you have to do on my pony, I'd be only too pleased to share him with you."

Fiona's eyes shone. All she could say was, "Oh, Stephanie, that would be great!" ●

Painting on Pebbles

Most people just take stones for granted — and why not? They're pretty boring things, on the whole! They don't *have* to be boring, however — with just a wave of your magic paintbrush, you can transform ordinary grey pebbles into really attractive objects. Often used as paperweights, painted stones can look just as nice simply as ornaments. You don't have to be an artist to paint pebbles — even the most abstract designs can look really good.

Pebble painting isn't an expensive hobby. First of all, of course, you must find your stones, but any beach or shallow river bed will yield an ample supply. So will pebble paths or driveways, but don't go raiding the garden without asking Dad's permission first! Large, flattish stones are easiest to work with at first, especially if you're painting an abstract design, but always keep an eye open for stones which suggest something to you — for example, if you decide to paint a bird, like one of our photographs, you could try to find a stone with ridges which resembled ruffled feathers, or one whose shape resembles a duck, and so on.

You will also need: paint (buy small tins of acrylic paint from handicraft shops) medium and fine paint brushes (proper sable paint brushes, such as artists use, are very expensive so stick to children's brushes) and varnish (again from handicraft shops).

Start by washing and thoroughly drying your chosen pebble. It should be large enough to paint on without difficulty — at least the size of a child's fist — and have a fairly smooth, flat surface. Now think about what you want to paint on your pebble. Don't be too ambitious to start with — a bold yet simple design, like the one shown here, would look very effective in the right colours — for example, red, white and blue.

First work out your design on paper, using felt tip pens in the same colours as your paints. When you are happy with the design, take a felt tip pen and carefully draw in the 'dividing lines' on the stone. Now simply paint all the areas of one colour — say, red, on one side of the stone, leave to dry and add the blue, and finally the white. When completely dry, turn over and paint the bottom of the stone in the same way. You don't have to paint both sides of the pebble, of course, but with an all-over design like this it's best to continue the pattern all the way round. Afterwards, varnish the whole stone with a

M EDWARDS

large paintbrush dipped in clear varnish.

You can try a more complicated version of this design using a paper stencil in patterns cut to your choice. Lay the stencil flat on the stone, paint the areas shown through the stencil, and lift off the paper carefully. Or simply use gummed

indeed. The puffin is the simplest of the three to copy, using bold areas of colour. The owl and the curlew are more difficult, involving delicate brushwork, but it's worth practising as the end result really is worth the time taken. Work out the design on paper first, to give you the 'feel' of the subject,

Lettering is done in the same way, using a magnifying glass. You will find it a lot easier to write the letters in pencil on the stone first and then paint over them with a fine brush, than to try to paint them on 'blind'.

You will probably be so pleased with the results of your painting that you will want to keep your pebbles for yourself, but they also make super presents, for everyone from grandparents to schoolfriends (don't give them to very young children, just in case they try to lick the varnish off!). Remember to paint your initials and the date on the base of each pebble.

M EDWARDS

paper shapes to mark off some areas while you paint others.

Now you're ready to try painting a picture on a pebble. Often the shape of a stone will suggest what to paint—a bent old woman or a curled, sleeping cat, perhaps. Or you could simply use large, flat stones as a background for your favourite subject. The lovely bird pebbles shown here, for example, are all painted on flat stones, and as you can see look very effective

then draw in fine outlines on the stone with a felt tip pen, or with a pencil if it will show up, before starting to paint.

Small, detailed work is best done with the help of a magnifying glass. Hold it steadily in your non-writing hand, lay the pebble flat on your working surface and carefully, using a very fine paintbrush, paint in the details. Always remember to let each colour dry completely before you go on to the next.

Once you've found out what an interesting hobby this is, you might like to try out various other ideas using pebbles, like making jewellery or mosaics from tiny polished stones, or making lamp bases by sticking small pebbles into plaster of Paris round a bottle. You can find out more about these hobbies from craft books in your local library.

So, you see, you're never alone with a stone! (ouch!)

The First Guide Handbook

Miss Agnes Baden-Powell wrote our very first Handbook in collaboration with her brother, Lord Baden-Powell, the founder of Guides and Scouts. It was published in 1912 and had nearly 500 pages of instructions, games and details of badges. Subjects dealt with included how to fell a tree, making mousetraps and what to do when you meet a mad dog!

At the time that the book was written, a lot of families were emigrating from Britain to Canada and other countries. Real 'pioneering' was necessary there in order to make a living in the undeveloped backwoods. So the Guide training programme would help to prepare girls for such an event. In fact, the book was called 'How Girls Can Help To Build Up The Empire', the Empire being the forerunner of our present Commonwealth.

Of course, most of the Guides remained in Britain and the contents included many things that we still do at Guide meetings today. The 'Baden-Powell Girl Guides', as they were known, were always well equipped to ensure that they could live up to the motto 'Be Prepared' and be ready to tackle any emergency. A new Company had first to cut out and sew their haversacks, flags, bandages, stretcher slings and camp ration bags, as well as 'their own skirts and knickers, serge from 7d (3p)'.

In those days, accidents caused by runaway horses were quite common, so every Guide had to know how to deal with this emergency. 'The way to stop a runaway horse is not to run out in front of it and wave your arms, but to try to race alongside it, catching hold of the shaft to keep yourself from falling. Seize the rein with the other hand and drag the horse's head round and so turn him that you can bring him up against a wall or a house, or otherwise compel him to stop.' It doesn't sound too easy, does it?

If faced with a mad dog, 'hold a stick, or even a handkerchief,

Miss Agnes Baden-Powell, President of the Girl Guides Association from 1910 to 1920 and a Vice-President until her death in 1944

in your two hands in front of you, and the dog will generally try to paw it down before he actually bites you, and you may thus get a chance of giving him a kick under the jaw.' What an extraordinary picture this conjures up! Can you imagine meeting a mad dog and giving him a kick under the jaw?

Camping was still a novelty to most people when Guides first started. No doubt many a parent felt dubious about such a venture for their daughter, but the camps were very well organised. A good secondhand tent could be bought for around £2, or you could make your own. The kit list included one woollen vest, a flannel nightdress or sleeping suit, one wool combination (!) and ration bags for sugar, tea, salt and pepper, flour and baking powder.

Meals have always been an

Two 1910 Guides and their Guiders practise first-aid

The 1st Burnage (Manchester) Guide Company in camp in 1915 at Abergele (Above)

A 1912 Guide Company (Right)

W MYERS

important part of camp. For the Cook badge you had to be able to cook various dishes, and to show that you could skin and clean a rabbit or pluck and truss a chicken!

A Guide had to pass her Second Class badge before she could take any of the 26 proficiency badges. Many of the syllabuses are on much the same lines as today. However, for Horsemanship you had to drive as well as ride a horse. For Flyer you had to make an aeroplane (presumably a model one!) to fly 25 yards, and have some knowledge of engines. Instead of aiming to be a Queen's Guide, Guides worked to gain a Silver Fish*. For this you had to gain the First Class badge and 19 proficiency badges. There is a special note for badge-testers in the instructions: 'They may not lay claim to any article produced for tests, such as tarts, cakes, flags, knickers, etc.'!

Guides were also taught to be very observant; some of the suggested games involved finding a hatpin in a field of grass, a pencil in a wood, or golf balls on a stony beach. Marks were deducted from your score in a game if you were not up to

*This very soon became an adult award for service to Guiding and remains so.

standard personally: '20 marks off for untidy waist, 30 marks off for hat off, 40 marks off for not saying Madam'.

Emphasis was always laid on helping the old and sick. 'Sweet singing is a great pleasure to invalids, when it is low and soft. Cultivate a voice like the wind singing in the boughs of trees,' advised Miss Baden-Powell.

Perhaps the old folk would have enjoyed watching the 'Fairies' Dance', which was another idea for a Company meeting. Ideally it was to be performed 'in a pretty glade, with branches of blossom in the hand, or garlands, scarves or fans.' Perhaps you could use this idea for your Entertainer badge? It might be fun to arrange an evening of activities from sixty years ago—look up library books for costume ideas, or ask your grandparents for some ideas.

Next time you go on a hike, do try 'Empress Eugenie's Circle', 'a good method of sitting down to rest when the weather is wet'. Stand in a ring with the tallest girls on one side and the smallest opposite, and the rest according to height. Put both hands on the shoulders of the girl next to you to the right. At a given signal, all sit down at

once on the knees of the person behind. 'All must wait for the signal to rise. Provided all do this promptly at the signal it is quite safe'. The instructions go on to say that staves (stout walking sticks) may be used in the outside hand to give a steadying effect. Patrol Leaders had their Patrol flag on their stave, and every Guide would carry one on a walk or if doing ambulance work.

The uniform must have been very hot in summer. The hat was a dark-blue Scout's felt, with a wide, flat brim and a chinstrap. The neckerchief was pale blue, 40 inches long, worn knotted at the throat—and also at the ends, until the good turn for the day was done. The shirt-blouse had two pockets with the Patrol crest sewn on the left front; the colour was chosen by the Company. Skirts were dark blue serge, again with two pockets. Stockings had to be dark blue or black 'worn drawn up tight over the knee'. A brown leather belt with two swivels, gauntlet gloves and black shoes or boots completed the outfit.

'By wearing a uniform a Guide shows that she is striving to be efficient' wrote Miss Baden-Powell, and her advice still holds good today.

ROLLUP, ROLLUP!

Bazaars and jumble sales are excellent fund raisers for a Guide Company, and the food stall is always a popular one. Your choice of food should be quick and cheap for you to make, easy for your customers to carry home, tempting to look at and, of course, delicious to eat!

'Old favourites' like fairy cakes always sell well, but here are some different ideas which should go—well, like hot cakes!

PIZZA ROLLS, ready to grill, are a super idea and easy to prepare. Buy a supply of those large, soft, 'bap' rolls and halve them. 'Butter' each half with tomato puree (available in tubes from supermarkets and delicatessens) and add a thick slice of cheese. Top with sliced olives, anchovies, salami, tinned mushrooms, onion rings, etc. Wrap in clingwrap film. You can make amusing children's versions of these pizzas by turning the topping into a face—make olive 'eyes', red pepper 'mouths' and 'noses', and mix grated cheese with a little tomato puree for 'hair'. Your customers just pop them under the grill for 5 minutes and they're sizzling hot and ready to eat!

'EXTRA' BISCUITS—the idea behind these biscuits is that you make up several batches of the mixture, each with a different 'extra' flavouring. So from the basic mixture, you can make:

Sultana cookies—add 1 oz chopped sultanas

Choc Chip cookies—add 1 oz chopped chocolate pieces

Cherry biscuits—add 2 ozs chopped glace cherries

Coconut drops—add 1 tablespoon desiccated coconut

Peanut biscuits—add 1 dessertspoon chopped peanuts

Chocolate drops—add 2 teaspoons powdered drinking chocolate

Cinnamon biscuits—add 1 rounded teaspoon cinnamon

Caraway cookies—add 1 heaped teaspoon caraway seeds

Nutmeg biscuits—add 1 teaspoon grated nutmeg

Or anything else you can think of!

Here's how to make the plain mixture. You will need: 4 ozs margarine, 1 beaten egg (size 3), 4 ozs caster sugar, 7 ozs plain flour.

Heat the oven to Gas No. 6/400°F. Beat the margarine and sugar together in a bowl with a wooden spoon until the mixture is pale and fluffy. Add the egg gradually, mixing well. Fold in the flour slowly, using a metal spoon, and add your chosen 'extra'. (You might need to add a little milk at this point if the mixture seems very dry.) Place teaspoonfuls of the mixture on a greased baking sheet and bake for ten minutes or until the biscuits are golden brown. Cool on a wire tray. This makes approximately 30 biscuits.

APPLE CHUTNEY—this is delicious and doesn't cost much to make, especially in autumn when apples are cheap.

Ingredients: 4 lbs cooking or semi-sweet eating apples; 2 pints brown vinegar; 1 teaspoon salt; 2 level teaspoons cinnamon; 2 lbs onions; 1 lb sultanas; $1\frac{1}{2}$ lbs soft brown sugar; 3 level teaspoons ginger; 6 cloves and a bay leaf, tied together in a small muslin bag.

Peel and slice the apples and onions. Chop roughly. Put into a saucepan with the sultanas and half the vinegar. Cover and simmer until the apples are soft (approx. 30 minutes). Add the remaining ingredients and simmer, stirring, until the sugar dissolves. Cook, with the lid off, till thick, stirring occasionally. Remove muslin bag and when the chutney is cool spoon it into yogurt cartons. Cover with clingwrap film and label.

HOME MADE SWEETS make lovely presents, if you sell them attractively packaged. The problem is that cooked sweets such as toffee and fudge are very difficult to make properly without lots of practice, so here are some no-cook sweets which are simple to make and look really pretty, too.

Coconut Ice: mix a small tin of condensed milk with enough dessicated coconut (about 4-5 ozs) to give a firm consistency. Press half the mixture into a greased baking tin, then colour the other half a delicate pink by mixing in 2-3 drops red food colouring. Press on top of the

other half of the mixture, spread level with a knife and leave to set. When hard, cut into small squares.

Peppermint Creams: beat an egg white until fluffy. Add 1 teaspoon peppermint essence and gradually stir in 10-12 ozs sifted sugar, until the mixture is very stiff. Colour pale green with 2-3 drops green food colouring and turn onto a working surface. Roll out until $\frac{1}{4}$inch thick and cut into small circles with an apple corer or bottle top. Roll out the trimmings and re-cut until all the mixture is used up. Leave for a few hours to set.

Vanilla Creams are made in the same way, substituting a teaspoon of vanilla essence for peppermint and a few drops of orange or yellow colouring for the green.

Marzipan Fruit: simply buy a block of ready made marzipan and divide it into 4 pieces. Colour the four pieces orange, red, yellow and green with food colouring. Then just break off small bits of marzipan and form into fruit shapes. It's very easy to do – make oranges from small round balls of orange marzipan, pressed against the side of a grater to give an orange peel effect. Strawberries are made from red 'triangles' of marzipan, 'dotted' with the tip of an orange stick to give strawberry markings. Bananas are easy – just curved pieces of yellow marzipan – you can paint on brown streaks with a paint brush dipped in brown food colouring or coffee essence. Lettuces are fun, but a bit more complicated – fashion leaves from green marzipan and stick 7 or 8 leaves onto a circle of marzipan to make a lettuce shape.

Stuffed Dates are simple to make too. Stone whole dates and fill the space left with a wedge of marzipan, topped with half a glace cherry.

Make up selections of all the above sweets and pack them prettily into flat boxes. The kind that notelets are packed in are ideal, as they come with transparent lids. Place the sweets in individual sweet cases (like tiny cake cases) first and fit them into the boxes. If the boxes do not have lids, make them from clingwrap film stretched smoothly over the top.

If you can persuade someone who is a very good cook to make a big iced cake for you, you can use this as a centrepiece for your stall *and* bring in extra funds by having a 'guess the weight of the cake' competiton, with the cake itself as the prize. You'll need lots of paper bags for this stall, so start saving them up well in advance.

Don't forget that walking around a hall or field full of people can be very tiring. Dilute a large container of orange squash and sell it in paper cups – even charging three pence or so a cup will bring in quite a big profit, and lots of thirsty bargain hunters will be very grateful to you!

The sound of church bells on a summer morning is familiar to us all. But few people know how they work and how they are built. In some churches there is only one bell in an outside open turret, but most bells you will find housed inside the belfry. Some churches have bell-ropes with their brightly coloured striped 'sallies', just inside the porch. At others they are in the ringing loft.

How are the hours sounded on a bell without anyone pulling the rope? Near the bottom of the bell there is a small spring-loaded hammer. This is connected by a wire to the clock works. When the clock registers the hour, the wire pulls on the hammer, causing it to strike the outside of the bell the required number of times.

Most bells carry an inscription of some kind, eg Alexander Rigbe Made Me 1680; God Save

BELLS

First, the inner mould or core has to be produced by a strickle template or crook. This will mould the outer surface of the core

The next step is to line the inner case with loam and another swinging template then moulds the cope or cover of the bell

The cope and core are finished by hand and put on a special stove to be dried. When this is done, the cope is placed over the core forming the mould

the Queen 1625; Cast by John Warner and Sons, London 1865. The inscription usually gives the maker's name and date of casting.

The history of bell making can be traced to the very early days of metal craft. Bells were probably introduced into the Christian Church by Paulinus, Bishop of Nola in Campania, Italy, which explains the Italian word 'campanile' (bell-tower), and 'campanolgy', which is the science of bell-ringing and founding. The making of bells has changed little over the centuries. To make a bell, a special mixture of metals is required, mainly copper and tin. As well as creating a very strong rust resistant metal this alloy ensures that the bell will have a good tone when struck.

Whitechapel Bell Foundry, renowned for bells such as America's Liberty Bell and the bells of Big Ben, has been casting for four hundred years.

Much of Whitechapel's work today consists of adding existing rings, retuning and melting down and re-casting cracked bells.

Church bells have many uses. In country parishes the 'pudding bell' used to ring at midday to warn housewives that their men would soon be returning from the fields for their dinners. Others used to sound a gleaning bell at harvest time. This was a signal that women and children could start picking up stray ears of corn to take.

Bells peal out joyfully for weddings and toll solemnly for a death. It used to be customary to toll three times three at the death of a man and three times five for a woman. This was followed by one stroke for each year of age. In this way the villager could quickly tell whose death it was likely to be. Hence the origin of the saying, 'Nine tailors (tellers) make a man'. Change-ringing grew popular during the 17th century. The art is to make the bell 'speak' in a particular numerical sequence. The greater the number of bells, the more changes can be included.

Bell ringing is still popular amongst people of all ages and today quite a few Guides join in the fun too.

The molten bell metal is poured into the mould at a temperature of about 1020°C. After casting the bell is trimmed, cleaned and drilled. By removing metal from different areas inside the bell on a lathe the strike note and tones are adjusted. This tuning process is now done electronically. Finally the fittings are added

It's Only Natural!

Cleopatra was reputed to have bathed in asses' milk every day . . . and we all know what a beautiful woman she was. And ever since Egyptian times, women have been using natural beauty aids as shampoos, cleansers, bath oils . . . there must be something in it! Chances are, though, that your milkman won't be too keen on the idea of delivering 80 or so pints of asses' milk to your doorstep every day! Don't despair, we have lots of other 'back to nature' ideas for you to try, most of which can be made from ingredients found in your own home. We'll let you into the secrets of the beauty kitchen—if you promise not to eat the ingredients!

LEMON JUICE – the juice of half a lemon is excellent for removing stains and ingrained dirt from hands.

VINEGAR – dilute 3 tablespoons of vinegar in a cupful of warm water. Pour over greasy hair as a final rinse.

MUSTARD – a pinch of dry mustard added to a hot bath is said to stave off a cold.

MILK – dip some cotton wool in a saucer of milk and wipe over your face. Rinse off after 2 or 3 minutes with cool water. Good for cleansing normal skins.

EGG YOLK – comb a beaten egg yolk through your hair after shampooing, to give a glossy sheen to dull hair. Rinse off with lots of *lukewarm* water – not too hot, or you'll end up with scrambled egg on your head!

BEER – after washing, wet the hair with beer and use as a setting lotion. It gives added body to the hair and helps the set to stay in.

NATURAL YOGURT is a good cleanser for greasy skins. Use as you would a normal cleanser, applied with cotton wool.

DRIED MILK – toss 2 or 3 tablespoons into your bath for a soothing, calming effect.

MIXED HERBS – place a selection of dried or fresh herbs in a small piece of muslin and tie under the bath tap so that the hot water runs over the bag and into the bath. This gives a fresh smelling and soothing bath.

GELATINE – Mix a tablespoon of powdered gelatine into your shampoo next time you wash your hair. Gelatine is full of protein so does wonders for damaged hair.

SALT – sprinkle salt on your toothbrush and brush your teeth as usual. You'll be amazed at how white and sparkling your teeth look!

LETTUCE—boil up some lettuce leaves in water for a few minutes, then press through a sieve. The resulting lotion is really effective in soothing sunburn.

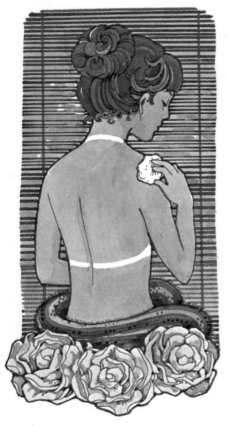

ORANGES AND LEMONS—chop up half a small lemon and half a large orange very finely (do not remove peel first) and put in a saucepan with a teaspoon of caster sugar and a cupful of milk. Heat to almost boiling point, leave to cool and sieve. Bottle and keep in the fridge. This makes a refreshing skin tonic for all skin types, to be used after cleansing the face.
EGG WHITE—beat an egg white till frothy and add a few drops of lemon juice. Spread on the face and leave for 15 minutes before rinsing off with cool water. Helps tone up greasy skin.

OLIVE OIL—heat about 2 ozs. of olive oil by standing the bottle in a basin of warm water for a while. Massage the oil well into your hair and scalp *before* washing your hair. Wrap a warm towel around your head and leave for 20 minutes or so before washing your hair with shampoo in the normal way. This is one of the best conditioners for dry hair, recommended by lots of top hairdressers. Repeat every 4th or 5th time you wash your hair.
PARSLEY—chewing a sprig of parsley will freshen the breath.

OATMEAL AND ORANGES—mix a tablespoon of fine oatmeal with a tablespoon of finely grated dried orange peel (leave it on a tray in a warm place to dry). Mix about a teaspoonful with a little warm water in your hands and use to wash your face with, rubbing the grains well into the skin. You will find these cleansing grains are ideal for very oily complexions.
WATER—yes, even plain water makes a terrific beauty treatment! Take a handful of sweet smelling dried herbs or flowers (eg. dried lavender) and toss them into a large bowl or basin of boiling water. Now put a large towel over your head (and the basin) and sit under this 'steam tent' for 10-15 minutes. This is an excellent way of 'unclogging' the pores and is highly recommended for skins

troubled by spots.

There are other ways of using water as a beauty treatment, too. Splashing lots of water on your face after cleansing it is an excellent toner for the skin — use icy cold water if your skin is greasy, lukewarm water if it is dry or normal. *Never* use cold water on dry skin, in case you break the tiny thread veins on your cheeks.

Drinking a glass of cold water, with a piece of lemon, first thing in the morning, will make you feel wide awake and ready to start the day. If you really can't face cold water first thing in the morning, though, do at least try to drink as much water as you can throughout the day — it will help you to a better skin and a brighter you!

The Wasp

A wasp flew to visit a Guide camp one day,
And he laughed at their efforts to drive him away.
He buzzed in the hair of the Cowslips' P.L.
And sat on the ear of the Q.M. as well.

He flew in the store tent and frightened poor Pam,
Who was fetching a large tin of strawberry jam;
She gave a loud shriek and dropped it and fled,
So he broke off the chase and ate jam instead.

All through supper he teased them and sat on the meat,
Which those hungry young campers were trying to eat;
But at last from that menace the camp was set free,
For the wasp met his end—in my cup of tea!

by Jean Howard

The Joys (?) of Camping

It's 4am and Tracey's awake
And now everyone else is too
With a "good morning" and a violent shake
"Isn't it fun, our first day at camp,
The sun is shining, though everything's damp,
And there's ever so much to do."

"Oh, *do* be quiet and go back to sleep"
That's Captain, a voice from the rear
"If you don't feel tired, try counting sheep!"
"Oh do as she says Tracey, turn out your lamp,
If you don't want to be removed from camp
Before we're properly here!"

Denise, June and Paula later aspire
To the dizzy delights of lighting a fire
Bacon and eggs is the day's first meal
Patrol cooking's fun—when it's for real.

Jill likes to see there's plenty of water
For washing (but oh how remiss
I don't think anyone has yet—but sh!
Don't tell—though really they oughter!)

All too soon the last night is here
As everyone sheds a communal tear
The sky lowers, and so do the colours.
Fancy dress parade, and would you believe
Jane and Ann are dressed up as the apple and Eve.

Time for bed and our midnight feast
Pity we fell asleep. . . .
Captain's finally taught us all
The art of counting sheep!

Up next morning, the air is bitter
Check the field for mess and litter
The coach arrives, equipment piled high,
Bedding rolls leave a lot to be desired!

Thank you Captain, Lefty and Q.M. too
For everything you had to do
To make Guiding and our camp such fun
We'll be back next year for another one!

by Kath Cure

Invitations are always exciting. Some are very special, like parties or weddings, and some are really very grand indeed, like those received by the Duke of Edinburgh's Gold Award winners. When we get one, there is always a hunt for the diary, a great checking of dates and a sigh of relief when the date is free. The next questions come into our heads thick and fast—what to wear? Any money for a new dress? How to get there? Who else will be going? What shall we do?

Our invitation to take part in the Royal Tournament at Earls Court Stadium brought all these problems, but in a VERY big way. Could it be done by the 19th of July—rather near the end of a busy term? Would exams be over in time to rehearse? To rehearse WHAT? How many people, and where from? What about clothes? And finally, as always, where would the money come from to make it really good?

If you have ever been to a Royal Tournament or Tattoo, you will remember at once all the exciting items—musical rides on horses or motor bikes, races between gun crews, helicopter and cliff face rescues, powerful gymnastic displays, laser beams playing in patterns, plus all sorts of dazzling and deafening effects, and all very military, all very highly polished and efficient. What a task to show the Girl Guide Movement to its best advantage in eight minutes against such a background! What could we do?

But the brainwave came—a 'tournament', a medieval tourney reconstructed with all the colours, sounds and effects we could contrive, which would fit into the frame of such a pro-

Trefoil

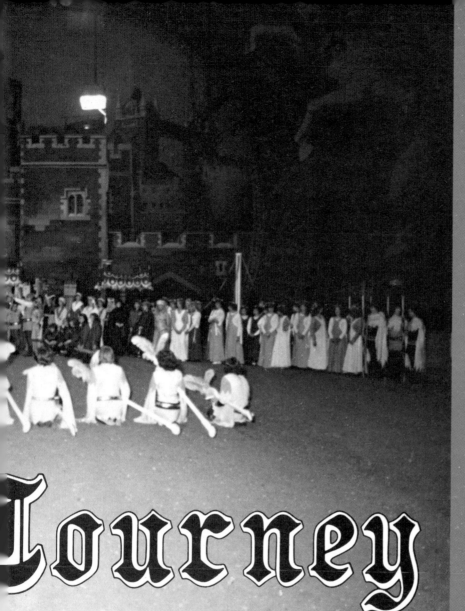

Journey

A scene from the very colourful and spectacular performance

Below far left: time for a photo call!

Below left: a grandstand view of the performers

gramme yet would show the performers in the most attractive costumes and setting. So 'Trefoil Tourney' was born.

At least two hundred and fifty girls would be needed to make a showing in the arena, and they must come from as many parts of the United Kingdom as was practicable. Money? Of course our Movement would back us to the hilt—it was a *first* in our history, after all—and sponsorship from a source familiar to many of our fund raising schemes—Webb Ivory—was very welcome. Girls from five regions were asked to take part and almost every county sent a group.

The Oxford Dictionary defines a tournament as 'a meeting at an appointed time for knightly sports and exercises'. *Our* appointed time was—in military terms—'H+59' on the afternoon of 19th July at Earl's Court in the presence of our President, H.R.H. the Princess Margaret, and of the Chief Commissioner, Mrs. Owen Walker.

A bird's eye view of the country early on that day would have shown many scattered little blobs, like blue mercury, gradually coalescing, joining with other blobs to make bigger ones—all rolling on their journey towards London, where somehow, in some way, they would resolve themselves into a moving picture, a whole programme at last.

Until the morning of the event, no group had the slightest idea of the scope or size of the exercise. York, Manchester, Cardiff, Leeds and Birmingham – these were the meeting places for rehearsing the various component parts, and very strange and detached they seemed. But it was here in the regions that the real work was done, the producers' ideas brought to life, the designer's version realised. In what was a very short time the transformation had taken place. Gone were the girls in jeans and T-shirts, eyeing each other and wondering. Here instead was a mob of peasants out for a rare day's fun, with its usual complement of good and bad, of nuns and pickpockets, of peddlars and lovers. And there we saw a stately procession – my Lord and Lady, their retinue and customary train of followers. There was the usual preliminary flaunting of rival wealth and property – the outriders displaying their superior mounts and horsemanship, and finally the two protagonists themselves – the Black and White Knights, plumed, caparisoned and armed cap-à-pie. But each group had to work on its own.

Space was totally inadequate for practice – the expanse of the arena at Earl's Court was enormous, its length equalling that of Salisbury Cathedral, and manoeuvres had to be tried out in playgrounds, playing fields, car parks, or anywhere for suitable space. The martial music on the tape was drowned by aeroplane and traffic noise, the processions disrupted in full flow by car drivers looking for their accustomed parking lots, their passengers round eyed at the windows. Hobby horses were not so easy to manage on polished floors or on a football field, and had a nasty effect on

Rehearsals were not achieved under the easiest of circumstances and had to be snatched wherever possible

the riders too – especially next day! But eventually the choreography was resolved, every member of the cast had been carefully and individually clothed, and imagination began to work.

So with high hopes and great expectations, the descent upon Earl's Court was on – first things first, of course – three hundred lunch packets, crisps and squash ('an army marches on its stomach'), followed by all the necessary backstage impedimenta – huge mirrors, coat racks, make up, equipment, etc., and as the groups of girls began to arrive, so did the 'props'. These were the contribution of South West region and it would surely have been impossible to outclass them. They were fantastic, from the plumed and harnessed hobby

horses, halberds, banners and trumpets with their intricate devices, ornate canopies, the maypole with rainbow ribbons, even to a pair of hawks to perch on the wrist of their trainer. And the ingenuity of their creation! There must still be some bewildered shopkeepers in the West Country. . . .

'*Twelve* paraffin funnels, Madam? . . . for *trumpets,* you said? Just as you say, Madam. . . .'

'Left handed gauntlets? Well, no – very little demand, Miss, not much hawking going on these days, you see.'

And the expedition to find a small shop behind Smithfield Market on pig killing day (ugh!) – the final stage in a search for horses' plumes – had its moments. 'Can it be? – Yes, at last, the absolutely ideal curled feather! How many shall

Every one of the three hundred members of the cast had a costume made especially for the Tournament

we need? Twenty four? Oh, did you say £25 *each*!?! Perhaps we had better take these smaller ones and curl them ourselves with Carmen rollers. . . .' Suffice it to say that the props were super—the crowning touch to the production.

Once we were inside, and had been frisked for bombs, we found that Earl's Court had its hazards. Dressing rooms were three floors up—no lifts for performers—and it was fatally easy to get lost. The main concourse was full of soldiers, bands, kiosks, tanks, armoured cars, helicopters, ropes and ladders. At 11.30 a.m. an attempt was made to put the bits of the jigsaw together. We held our breath . . . would it work? Would the cues be clear? Had we got our props? The amplified opening bars of the tape came over

and we were off. Entries, lighting, spacing, speed, positioning—a quick run over all these, final instructions and encouragement from the producer, a photo call and the time was up.

The floor manager's instructions too had been very clear, and a self-disciplined cast removed all their costumes and settled down to a picnic lunch of sandwiches, sausage rolls, crisps, apples and squash before the real business began. Every performer had to be made up suitably and adequately for the strong arena lighting, but with patience and the minimum of queueing everyone assumed her new face, costumes were checked and good wishes exchanged.

The moment had arrived—it was 'H+59' at last.

How to describe our feelings

as we gathered by the arena entrances? Excited? Of course, but alert and keyed up to give the performance of our lives.

The effect was stunning—a kaleidoscope of blues, yellows, greys and silver—all the creative planning, the lighting, colour, costumes, music, transforming performers and setting into a magical presentation. The crowd ebbed and flowed, the maypole ribbons twirled, till at the sound of the trumpet the masses parted to make way for the banners, the halberdiers, the outriders. With a surge and a swish of robes, lords and ladies, bishops and acolytes, attendants and followers swept up to the canopied dais. The Black and White Knights, in a hush of tense expectation, prepared to joust. . . .

The audience loved every minute of it, for it was a truly captivating performance.

Why, we were asked, was the Girl Guides' item so much shorter than the others? In fact, it certainly was *not*, but the allocated eight minutes were so packed with detail and content, and the idea so fresh and original, that it passed like a flash. The cast thoroughly deserved the great ovation it received as everyone circled the arena on the way out, giving a final wave to the Royal Box.

So ended 1979's most ambitious event—an occasion when the Girl Guides Association presented itself to the public in a very unusual and attractive way, when the Movement showed what ingenuity, co-operation and dedication could do, and when, best of all, we shared a memorable experience. Echoing one performer's words:

'It was the happiest day in my Guide life'.

a day

7.30 a.m. Race you to breakfast!

10.30 a.m. There must be an easier way to get out of camp!

at

12 noon. Just hanging around...

3 p.m. A woman's work is never done!

camp

5.30 p.m. A quick dip before tea.

8.30 p.m. I'm so tired, I can't walk a step further!

Have you been able to decipher the message above? In boating International Code Flags are used for signaling. These flags not only stand for a specific letter but have another meaning too. Flags are not always used – sometimes it's a morse code letter. Have you deciphered the codes in your Handbook? Here are some stories to help people remember the flags and their meanings – they really are quite amusing!

These are the meanings when the flags are used as special signals on their own but they change once again when used in combinations of two, three, four or even five letters. Fascinating, isn't it? How much more can you find out?

If you do ever get involved in boating, you find that lots of words have another meaning!!

C stands for Charlie. He is very fond of layer cake (does this flag remind you of one?) and whenever it is offered he always says 'yes, please' and has some. This flag is the 'Yes', or Affirmative, one.

N in the phonetic alphabet is November. This flag symbolises 'No' the first two letters of the longer word; and can you see the snow flakes in the blue sky we expect at this time of the year?

O is called Oscar and he is famous as the ship's fool! The ship's deck is the yellow part and it looks like there is a rough sea at the moment and the red sky shows it is stormy. Oscar – being typical – has gone over the side – and thus this means Man Overboard!

I stands for India and in this flag we have a small Indian boy stranded in the desert. All he has to drink is a bottle of port. This means 'I am altering my course to port' (ie. to the left).

A PAINTER isn't someone who is going to make your house look new, it's a . . .

A FLY isn't a pest with wings, it's . . .

A STRETCHER isn't something the injured are carried away on, it's . . .

THWART isn't to frustrate or defeat someone it's . . .

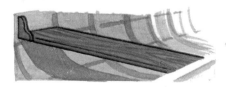

SHEETS are not things you sleep between – they are . . .

A BOOM is not the noise cannons make, it's . . .

ROWING

Learning how to row as part of a crew with several others can be great fun and learning how to respond to these orders can be like learning another language!

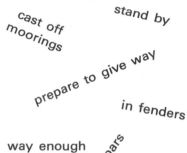
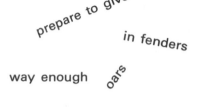

cast off moorings

stand by

prepare to give way

in fenders

way enough

oars

What shall I wear?? You will need to think very carefully about what you will wear depending on the type of boating you will be doing, but one vital thing when canoeing and sailing will be your lifejacket. This should be a B.S.I. approved type.

You will need to learn how to put it on properly and tie it tightly using the correct knot. If you do need to swim while wearing it, it is best to do side stroke or swim on your back.

CANOEING

Canoeing is not always as easy as it looks and even to manage to paddle in a straight line for the beginner can be a big achievement.

Keep practising though, until you are proficient enough to tackle that white water at the weir or go canoe camping—where you have all your possessions with you and look after yourself in the great out of doors where you choose to stop for the night—great fun!

measuring paddle

canoeing with lifejacket and helmet on

spray deck

helmet

SAILING

What a feeling to have the wind carrying you and your boat along at exciting speeds and sometimes at exciting angles too!

You are at the mercy of the wind, but at the same time learn to use it to your best advantage. You can't sail directly into the wind but can learn to zig-zag to get where you would like to be!

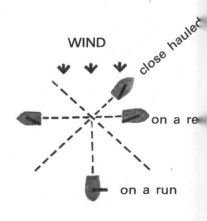

WIND

close hauled

on a re

on a run

Happy boating!

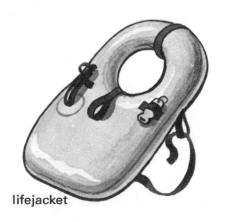

lifejacket

30

Myth, Music and Magic

Arts activities are great fun. We proved it at a weekend workshop held by the North Tyneside Guides.

Forty-five Guides came from all over North Tyneside. The workshop was organised by the county arts team. The theme the girls worked around was that of a local legend—a simple one with an uncomplicated story-line. It gave the Guides plenty of scope for using their own initiative and imagination.

Briefly the legend told of days long ago when a small boy's dream came true. Growing up, the boy becomes a knight and returns to the small fishing community of his childhood. There he overcomes the monsters that have long guarded a hidden treasure. The treasure lay for hundreds of years hidden within a cavern deep in the cliffs beneath Tynemouth Priory.

This was the story the Guides dramatically re-created with masks, monsters and music. The art group had a marvellous time producing a variety of monsters and horrific monster masks. If your Company plan to produce a drama on somewhat similar lines the drawings on this page should help you to make masks and a monster mobile.

The masks were built up on a simple card base (see drawing A), which, before being decorated, was adjusted and fastened to fit snugly on the wearer's head, allowing freedom of movement. Scrap material was used in the making of the masks. When complete each mask was varnished with a P.V.A. medium to give a good finish and extra strength. Two Guides made the brave knight's helmet, armour and sword, whilst a further group worked together producing large snake-like mobiles. These were made by cutting the cardboard inner tubes of carpet-rolls into small sections. Heads and tails were built up on four of the sections, then all the pieces were painted in bright colours and patterns. The sections were then strung together (see drawing B) and suspended between two poles.

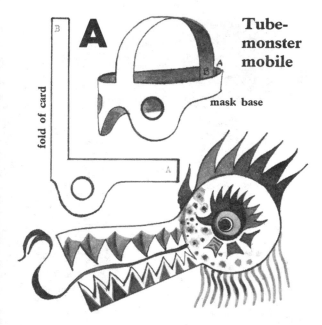

A

fold of card

B

mask base

Tube-monster mobile

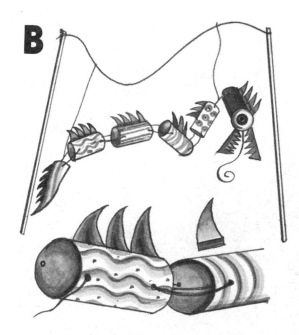

Working on tube-monster mobile

A finished mask   Some of the cast in the play

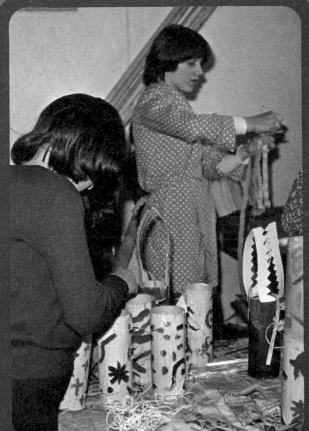

The music group produced wonderful sound effects, live and on tape. Unlikely objects and instruments were used to produce the sounds of the seashore and of storms: jews-harps, bottle-tops, rattles, and so on. Human voices produced some marvellous sounds on tape too. Local folk-songs were sung as by a band of travelling minstrels, and the dance and drama were accompanied by both tape and performed music. Instruments played included recorders, guitars and violins, but in addition a great variety of home-made instruments was used.

Three Guides produced beautifully made cane-rattles, whilst others made tambourines, maracas and Japanese drums (see drawing C). It was proved that you do not have to be a proficient musician to participate in musical activities.

Everyone in the group was included in the actual production, and all types of ability were utilised. Costumes and props had to be planned. Costumes, it was proved, can be made out of the simplest of materials.

At various times throughout the weekend the three groups —music, dance/drama and arts/crafts—met together to discuss progress. This enabled everyone to understand what everyone else was doing and problems to be ironed out.

The final run-through was enormous fun for everyone. Although far from perfect, the performance of the play produced a wonderful feeling of achievement in all involved. New friendships were made, and the Guides found out for themselves how various arts activities integrate and can really be fun.

Perhaps your Company could run your own arts workshop or join with others in doing so.

JAPANESE DRUM

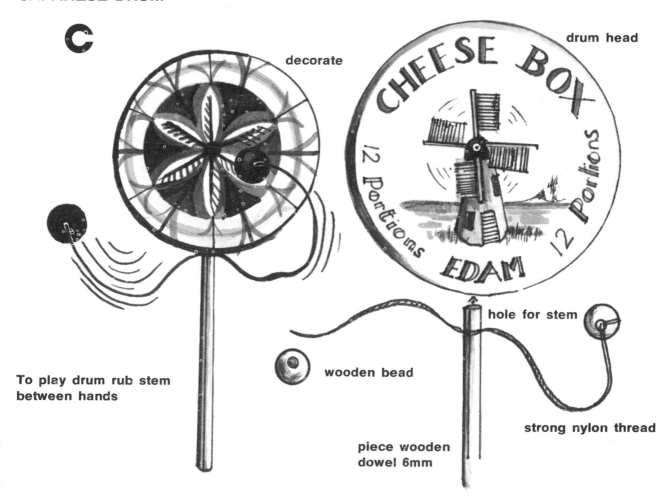

C

decorate

drum head

CHEESE BOX

12 Portions

12 Portions

EDAM

To play drum rub stem between hands

wooden bead

hole for stem

strong nylon thread

piece wooden dowel 6mm

DOG IN THE RAIN

It was dark and the rain sheeted down interminably as Louisa pushed her sister, Beth, in the wheelchair from Guides. It was ages since Beth had been able to attend a Guide meeting. She had had a lot of trouble since she had broken her leg. Now, hopefully, the last operation had put it right, although she was still not allowed to stand on it.

The rest of the Snowdrop Patrol waved goodnight. "So glad you could come again, Beth," called the Patrol Leader, Naomi. "Hope to see you next week."

"That was lovely, Louisa," said Beth. "Thanks so much for taking me tonight."

Louisa walked quickly on through the rain, past the shops where they usually lingered, holding her umbrella over Beth. Suddenly she stopped. From one of the doorways came a soft whimpering noise.

"What is it?" called Beth from the chair.

Louisa dropped to her knees in the doorway. "It's a poor dog," she said. "It's been hurt." The dog looked up at her and began to lick her hand. "Oh, Beth, its leg is bleeding. What shall we do?"

"Take it home," replied Beth promptly.

"But we can't," said Louisa. "It doesn't belong to us."

"We'll take it home, look after it, and advertise it," said Beth. "Can you lift it up beside me?"

Louisa gently lifted the dripping dog into the chair, and they

The dog looked up at her and began to lick her hand

made their way home.

"We must advertise it straight away," their mother said, after they had bathed the dog's leg and fed him. "Someone will be very upset at losing such a fine dog."

"If he had been mine I should never have lost him," declared Beth.

For a week Beth did everything she could to look after the dog. She called him Prince. No one answered the advertisement. When the Snowdrop Patrol heard what had happened, they began to save their pocket-money to help buy food for Prince. The dog proved a blessing to Beth, who gained a new interest in looking after him. For many months she had been looked after, and now she could look after something herself.

Then it happened. Their advertisement was answered.

Beth was in hospital again for a short stay, so she heard nothing about it.

When the doorbell rang, Louisa answered it. A man stood on the doorstep. "My name is Rogers," he said pleasantly. "I believe you have found a dog." At the sound of his voice, Prince ran out. He obviously knew the man. He wagged his tail and put his paws up against the visitor. "His name is Friend," Mr Rogers explained. "His owner is in hospital, and I've been away for several weeks. James hasn't missed him, but he'd be terribly upset if he found he was missing when he came out of hospital. Now, how much do I owe you for taking care of Friend?"

"Nothing," replied Mrs Marsh. "He's been a great help to my other daughter, Beth, and she'll miss him badly, I'm afraid;

34

but of course he must go back to his proper owner, and I'm sure Beth will be glad that he has found his right home."

Beth wasn't at all glad when she came out of hospital and heard that Prince had gone. She was furious.

"I was longing to see him again," she cried. "I thought of him a lot while I was in hospital. You shouldn't have let him go just like that. How can you be certain the man wasn't an impostor? Prince is a valuable dog, and this man Rogers might easily have called on the off-chance that he could get a fine dog for nothing."

"But Prince knew him," Mrs Marsh pointed out mildly.

Beth would not be comforted. She brooded over the loss of her dog, to the detriment of progress to full recovery of her health. Mrs Marsh became quite worried and thought of acquiring another dog as a pet for Beth. Then something unexpected happened. The Guides were to hold a jumble sale to raise funds for summer camp. Louisa and Beth spent several evenings collecting from houses, having left notification that they would be doing so. Calling at the end house of a terrace, they were greeted by loud barks, and when the door was opened a dog ran out. It was Prince.

"Prince!" cried Beth. "It's Prince!"

Prince jumped up, barking delightedly and wagging his tail furiously.

"You seem to know my dog," said the tall, spare man who had opened the door.

"Yes, he was lost and we took him in and I became very fond of him," said Beth, still stooping down and stroking and patting the dog. "I was really very sorry when I came out of hospital and heard that a Mr Rogers had claimed him. Are you Mr Rogers?"

Louisa spoke. "No, this isn't Mr Rogers, Beth."

Something in Louisa's tone made Beth look up. Till now she had not looked at the man who had opened the door, all her attention being concentrated on the dog. Now she saw that the tall, spare man, the owner of Prince, was blind.

"I can understand you being fond of Friend," said the man. "He's a very intelligent and affectionate dog. I couldn't do without him. He's my guide-dog."

"I—I didn't know," stammered Beth. "I'm very glad you got him back, Mr——"

"Coles is my name. My good friend Tim Rogers told me Friend had injured his leg and that some good people took him in. I'm glad to have the chance of saying thank you to you. I don't know what I'd do without Friend."

"I thought I couldn't do without him," murmured Beth, "but I see now that you need him more than I do, much more."

Collecting the jumble Mr Coles kindly fetched for them, the two girls made their way thoughtfully home.

"I'm going to suggest that the next jumble sale we have should be to raise money for a guide-dog," said Beth. "You know, Louisa, I can't say how thankful I am that Mr Rogers answered that advertisement. I'm happy about Prince now."

'Prince!' cried Beth. 'It's Prince!'

Of Course You Can!

"I've always wanted to be able to make soft toys – they make lovely presents and they do sell well when our Patrol has a coffee evening, but I can't sew."

Nonsense – anyone can make a rosette!

In thin material (cotton is best) cut out a circle about 10 cm in diameter.

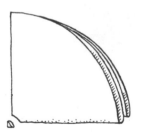

Fold it in four, and snip the point so as to make a small hole in the centre.

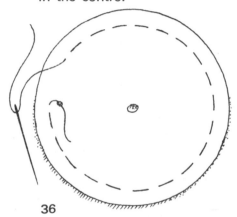

Run a gathering thread round the outside, pull it up until the cut edges meet in the middle and fasten off *very* securely.

If you can make one you can make some more; thread them on to thin elastic and in no time you have the basis of a variety of toys – especially if the rest of your Patrol joins in. A snake is the easiest to start with:

Cut out a cardboard circle 10 cm across to draw round (this is called a template and saves a lot of measuring). You will also need: a large bead or a button with a shank;

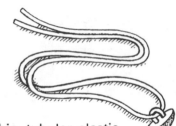

thin tubular elastic, twice as long as you want the snake to be;

two circles of felt or plain material for the head;

remnants of material in bright patterns and colours – cotton is easiest to work with but anything will do provided it is all of the same thickness.

First make your rosettes (10 cm of elastic will make about 15 rosettes) and decide the order in which you are going to arrange them.

Thread the bead or button on to the elastic and bring the ends together; thread rosettes on the double elastic and tie the ends securely in a large knot. Cut out two circles 7-10 cm across for the head; embroider or draw with feltpen a face on one, sew the two together leaving a 2 cm gap, turn right side out and stuff with cut-up scraps of material.

Tuck the elastic knot inside the head and finish sewing it up, taking some stitches through the elastic and some through the last rosette so that

the cut edges are hidden.
This part will get a lot of hard wear, so make sure it is well done.

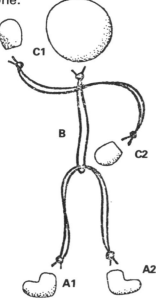

A toy with legs is slightly more complicated but made in the same way.

This is the basic framework—you have to decide whether you are making a doll or an animal, and how long the body and legs are to be.

You also need larger rosettes for the body than for the legs, so work this out as well and cut out cardboard templates. (The circles you cut out must be twice as large as the finished rosettes, remember.)

Make all the rosettes before starting to thread them on the elastic.

Make the legs and arms first; tie a large knot at A1, start to thread on small rosettes with the cut edges nearer to the knot; when you have got halfway thread them on the other way round. Finish off with another large knot at A2.

Make C1 and C2 in the same way.

Find the halfway point on elastic A, slip elastic B round and

bring the ends together; thread on the large rosettes with the cut edges down as before. When you have two left, put elastic C through elastic B as you did for A, add the last two rosettes and finish off with a knot.

Cover each knot with head, hands and feet as described for the snake.

WOOL

Dolls: cut out head, hands and feet as shown in the diagram, of a suitable size for the doll you are making, two pieces in each case. Sew together and then stuff each hand, foot and head until firm. Add wool for hair—either loops or plaits; a girl could have pink or white legs and a gathered skirt.

Or add a hat to the head before sewing up; give a clown large white frills at neck, wrists and ankles and a very bright face; a soldier could have a red body and arms with black or navy legs and hat to match (or made of fur if you can find a scrap).

Animals' feet are made so that they will stand up: cut two oval pieces for each foot and make a slit in one; sew together and turn right side out through the slit. Stuff, and sew up the slit, tucking the elastic knot through at the last minute and fastening off in the usual way.

These are the patterns for making animal heads. Copy them on to paper first, using larger squares to give the size you need. (Ask your Guider or another adult if you are not sure what this means.)

Sew together matching the letters.

Tiger: make a fabric tail, draw stripes on head, feet and tail with feltpen.

Elephant: make a plaited tail.

Lion: make a plaited tail. Make the two rosettes next to the head much larger, for his mane, and in fur if you can.

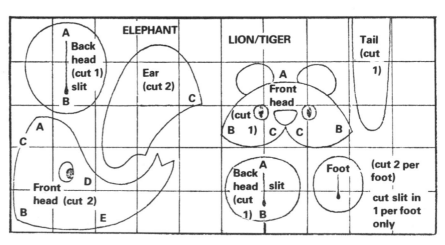

Hints For Campers

Every Guide who is working for her Camper badge must have camped 'at least twice and have spent not less than seven nights in Guide Camps'. Even if you're not working for this badge, however, it's a good idea to go to camp anyway as it really is one of the very best parts of Guiding.

Here are some ideas to make life at camp comfortable, as well as fun!

Before you set off for camp, you will be given a Kit List. Give the items on the list a little thought before you pack them—you don't want to turn up with all the wrong sorts of equipment! For example, never take china plates or cups to camp; they always get broken.

Tin items are much better, and will last for years. Take two plates—one flat and one deep, for soup and so on, and try to find a really big mug which will hold half a pint or more. Mark your cutlery with sewn on name tapes or with a paint which you are *sure* will not come off, and don't forget that your plate/cutlery bag should be easily identifiable too. Thread it with a drawstring to hang it up by, and remember that it should be made of a tough material that will not wear easily and can be placed under hot enamel plates, to save burning bare knees!

Camp can be a very miserable place unless you're warm enough in bed at night. Spending the night awake and shivering is guaranteed to make you feel rotten the next day, so make up your bed carefully.

You should put almost as much blanket underneath you as on top, and, of course, *always* put your bed on a groundsheet. Warm pyjamas and a woolly jumper are already mentioned on the kitlist, but it's also a good idea to take a pair of thick knee length socks with you, as you will find that the whole body rapidly cools down if the feet are cold.

One very important point to remember at camp is that damp quickly rises up through the ground, and kit gets soaked if it is not kept off ground level. So one of the first things you will do after your arrival is make yourself some gadgets to keep your kit dry. It will help if you can bring some suitable green (as opposed to dead) wood with you to camp—forked sticks and longish straight pieces of wood

are best. Three sticks of similar length and thickness, lashed together, will make a tripod which will take a rucksack, kitbag or bedding roll. It is usually easier for each member of the Patrol to have a separate tripod for her kit, but for everyone to share a bedding rack. This can be made simply by hammering four forked sticks into the ground and placing two rough poles between them. This can then be repeated, raising one of the bars slightly above the other, to make a shoe-rack.

You will also need a gadget in the wash tent for your toilet bags and towels. A tall tripod will hold a washing up bowl adequately, but not so tall to be out of reach of smaller members of the Patrol.

An electric torch is *essential* at camp, the more powerful the better. It should be kept by you at night, wrapped in polythene to prevent it getting damp.

Whatever else you might forget, don't go to camp without your 'wellies'! They are invaluable in the early mornings, and, of course, when it's raining. Don't take anything to camp that might be spoiled by dirt or damp – your best sweaters, for example.

Hats are always getting lost in camp, so put up a forked stick, or a stick with a crossbar attached to it, and make a point of always keeping your hat on it. This will save you time, trouble and maybe Patrol Points.

Don't forget to bring plenty of string and a sharp penknife. You will find all sorts of uses for them.

When you have been to several camps at home, try to go to an International one. They're great fun, and it gives a Guide an excellent chance to meet Guides from other countries and learn all about Guiding in different parts of the world.

Whether you are going camping for the first or the umpteenth time, I hope these few hints will be of some use to you. The Guide publication 'Hints On Guide Badges – Camper, Pioneer' offers more detailed help.

Remember to leave nothing behind but your thanks!

ENTERTAINING EPITAPHS

If you take the time one day to look at the epitaphs on gravestones in town and country churchyards, you will be surprised and often amused by what you read. You will also be helping your Patrol to gain the Explorer Pennant, for part of which you can choose to track down three interesting epitaphs or inscriptions on monuments,

Many people have felt that an epitaph should be in verse, and have tried hard to make up a good rhyme—not always successfully! A gravestone in Gloucestershire tells a sad little tale:

Here lie two babbies dead as nits,
Who died in agonising fits;
They were too good to live with we,
So God did take to live with he.

One from Crail, in Scotland, reads:

Here lies my good and gracious Aunty
Whom Death has packed in his portmanty. . . .

Sorrowing Australian parents wrote:

God took our flower—our little Nell;
He thought He too would like a smell.

Some epitaphs recall the deceased person's occupation. At Bromsgrove in Worcestershire you can find a long verse about an engine driver, while at Bolsover, Derbyshire lies:

. . . in a horizontal position,
The outsize case of Thomas Hinde,
Clockmaker and watchmaker,
Who departed this life, wound up, in hope of being taken in hand by his Maker, and being thoroughly cleaned, repaired, and set a-going in the world to come.

People often mistrusted millers, who had the reputation for keeping for themselves some of the best grain, but this epitaph was written in the last century at Wanborough in Wiltshire:

God works wonders now and then;
Herè lies a miller, an honest man.

Sudden and unexpected deaths are often recorded in verse, such as this one from Devon:

There was a man killed by lightning
Just when his prospects seemed to be brightening. . . .

In Sutherland, Scotland, you can read about John Flye:

Who did die
By a stroke from a sky-rocket
Which hit him in the eye-socket.

Some tombstones indicate that all was not well between husband and wife:

Here lies my poor wife
W'out bed or blankit,
But dead as a door nail,
God be thankit.

Or what about:

How snug in her grave my wife doth lie,
Now she's at rest, and so am I.

FLIPOT ZOOT, CAMERA PRESS

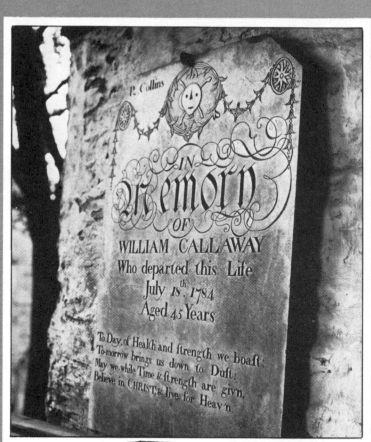

R.I.P.

At Porlock, Somerset, husband and wife seem to have been better suited:

He first departed; she for one day tried
To live without him, liked it not and dy'd.

The writer Charles Lamb once remarked that he wondered where all the bad people were buried. According to many descriptions on gravestones, it would appear that they were all too good to live! However, you can find the grave of a notorious Essex highwayman at Nayland, and of a Dorset man killed while smuggling tea near Bournemouth.

Some people, of course, go to much greater lengths than simply having a rhyme written about them. Look at these two London 'gravestones' shown here . . . the melody lingers on? After all, though, when all's said and done:

Praises on tombs are trifles, vainly spent,
A man's good name is his best monument.

Probably the most impressive epitaphs of all are the short ones which sum up a man's life in a sentence or so. That of Sir Christopher Wren, the architect of St Paul's Cathedral, is a Latin one which means:

If you seek his monument, look about you.

KATHRYN HAD FIRST MET HELGA LARSEN AT AN INTERNATIONAL GUIDE CAMP, AND WAS NOW TO SPEND THE LAST TWO WEEKS OF THE SUMMER HOLIDAYS AT HELGA'S HOME IN NORWAY. ONE MORNING, ALONG WITH HELGA'S ELDER BROTHER, NILS, THE GIRLS WENT UP INTO THE MOUNTAINS TO FISH FOR SALMON WHILE NILS, A VENTURE SCOUT, HOPED TO GET SOME SPECIMENS FOR A GEOLOGICAL PROJECT BEING CARRIED OUT BY HIS UNIT...

CLOSE ENCOUNTERS

LATER THAT MORNING HEAVY THUNDERCLOUDS ROLLED IN OVER THE PEAKS—AND SUDDENLY A FLASH OF LIGHTNING SPLIT THE DARKENING SKY...

HADN'T WE BETTER GET NILS AND HEAD FOR HOME?

THIS IS NO PLACE TO BE CAUGHT IN A STORM.

WITH THE SNOW SO UNSTABLE AFTER THE HOT WEATHER WE'VE BEEN HAVING.

MOMENTS LATER THE STORM BROKE...

QUICK! LET'S MAKE FOR THAT HUT! COME ON KATHRYN, HURRY!

BUT SUDDENLY THE GUIDES STOPPED IN THEIR TRACKS...

WHAT'S THAT NOISE?

IT'S AN AVALANCHE AND NILS IS RIGHT IN ITS PATH!

SECONDS LATER IT WAS THE GIRLS' TURN TO SCRAMBLE...

THAT SPUR OVER THERE—IT'S OUR ONLY CHANCE!

THEY MADE IT—JUST!

GRADUALLY THE AVALANCHE LOST MOMENTUM, AND ALL WAS QUIET AGAIN. BUT WHERE WAS NILS...?

THERE'S NO SIGN OF HIM! HE—HE JUST VANISHED!

BUT HE MUST BE HERE SOMEWHERE—HE MUST!

OVER THERE SOMETHING IS MOVING!

THEY PICKED THEIR WAY ACROSS THE TREACHEROUS SNOW

YES, IT'S NILS! COME ON HURRY!

THEY DUG THE SNOW AWAY WITH THEIR HANDS— AND PULLED HIM OUT, EXHAUSTED BUT ALIVE.

OH NILS, THANK GOODNESS YOU ARE ALL RIGHT.

THE THREE HEADED FOR SHELTER IN A MOUNTAIN CAVE.

YOU'RE SURE YOU'RE ALL RIGHT?

YES, I MANAGED TO KEEP NEAR THE SURFACE BY 'SWIMMING' AGAINST THE SNOW.

LISTEN! WHAT'S THAT NOISE?

WHAT ON EARTH...

WHAT GOOD LUCK! THREE STRONG YOUNGSTERS THAT I CAN MAKE USE OF!

LOTTE. I HAVE FOUND THREE HELPERS. QUICK, YOU! PICK UP THAT BOX AND NO TRICKS.

KATHRYN STAGGERED UNDER THE WEIGHT OF THE BOX.

NOW HURRY! WE MUST REACH THE BOAT BEFORE NIGHTFALL.

AS THEY TOOK UP THEIR POSITIONS, NILS WAS ALREADY SCHEMING TO TURN THE TABLES...

AT THE TREE LINE — BE PREPARED!

QUIET! NOW MOVE ALONG THERE.

THE TERRIBLE JOURNEY BEGAN. THEY WERE ALREADY COLD, TIRED AND HUNGRY, AND THE WEIGHT OF THE BOXES WAS UNBEARABLE. THEY FINALLY REACHED THE RIVER, THEN ON DOWNWARDS BY THE TRACK THAT LED TO THE VALLEY BELOW...

NILS HAD GUESSED THEY WOULD TAKE THIS ROUTE— AND AS THEY ENTERED THE FIR-TREES HE ACTED QUICKLY...

LOOK, THE SNOW— IT'S MOVING AGAIN!

WHAT...

SUDDENLY NILS GRABBED A LOW BRANCH AND AS THE GUNMAN TURNED...

AAAAAAGH!

I'LL TAKE THE GUN...

I DON'T THINK OUR FRIEND CAN WALK SO WE WILL SIT HERE WHILE YOU TWO GIRLS GO DOWN TO THE VALLEY AND BRING BACK SOME HELP.

THE GIRLS HURRIED ON DOWN THROUGH THE FOREST...

WE MUST BE QUICK, KATHRYN. NILS MUST STILL BE FEELING WEAK.

BUT SUDDENLY..

OOOH...

MY—MY ANKLE! I THINK I'VE TWISTED IT. YOU'LL HAVE TO GO ON ALONE.

ALL RIGHT, BUT FIRST LET'S PUT A BANDAGE ROUND THAT SWELLING.

KATHRYN SET OFF, BUT SOON THE DENSE TREES AND DARKENING SKY MADE IT MORE DIFFICULT TO FIND THE WAY. SHE BEGAN TO FEEL FRIGHTENED...

OH DEAR, WHICHEVER WAY I LOOK THE LANDSCAPE LOOKS THE SAME...

BUT THEN SHE REMEMBERED HER COMPASS — AND THE LANDMARKS SHE HAD NOTED ON THE WAY UP TO THE RIVER THAT MORNING...

I CAN HEAR THE RIVER OVER THERE, AND THAT RUNS IN A SOUTH WESTERLY DIRECTION. SO I SHOULD REACH THE VALLEY ON A WESTERLY COURSE.

KATHRYN WAS THANKFUL FOR HER COMPASS WORK AT THE GUIDES.

HELP IS ON THE WAY!

OH, BUT SUPPOSING THEY DON'T SPEAK ENGLISH? I'M SURE I SHALL NEVER BE ABLE TO MAKE ANYONE UNDERSTAND!

BUT AS SHE RACED ON, SHE THOUGHT OF ANOTHER PROBLEM.

MINUTES LATER, SHE WAS THERE...

JA, HVAD ER DET?

JEG ER ENGLANDER... ENGLISH... I NEED HELP!

FORTUNATELY, THE FARMER'S WIFE SPOKE ENGLISH — AND WITHIN MINUTES A PARTY OF MEN WAS ON ITS WAY...

I REALLY FEEL I SHOULD BE GOING WITH THEM...

YOU ARE NOT TO WORRY— NOW COME IN AND HAVE SOME HOT SOUP, YOU MUST BE EXHAUSTED.

TO KATHRYN THE WAIT SEEMED LIKE AN ETERNITY. BUT THREE HOURS LATER THERE WAS A CLATTER OF BOOTS OUTSIDE...

HELGA! NILS ARE YOU ALL RIGHT?

SOON THE POLICE ARRIVED, AND AFTER THE GUNMAN AND HIS ACCOMPLICE HAD BEEN QUESTIONED...

I WONDER WHAT WAS IN THOSE METAL BOXES?

DO YOU THINK THE POLICE OFFICER WOULD TELL US?

THE FARMER'S WIFE SPOKE WITH THE POLICEMAN, AND SOON SHE WAS ABLE TO EXPLAIN...

APPARENTLY THE BOXES CONTAINED COINS AND JEWELS HIDDEN DURING THE GERMAN OCCUPATION IN THE SECOND WORLD WAR.

IT SEEMS THEY FOUND AN OLD DIARY WITH A MAP INSIDE DESCRIBING HOW TO FIND THE BOXES. THE POLICE WILL RETURN THE VALUABLES WHEN THEY HAVE TRACED THE OWNERS.

THEY WERE GOING TO SHOOT US ONCE WE WERE DOWN THE MOUNTAIN AND PEOPLE WOULD THINK WE HAD DIED IN THE AVALANCHE.

GOOD THING YOU THOUGHT OF USING THAT BRANCH! IT SAVED OUR LIVES.

SEVERAL TIMES, I HAVE WALKED INTO THAT BRANCH, WHEN COMING DOWN THAT PATCH! I'M THANKFUL FOR IT NOW.

SO AM I!

ME TOO!

EVERYONE LAUGHED WITH RELIEF.

"NESSIE"

This photograph of 'Nessie' taken by Mr P A MacNab in 1955 has withstood thorough scientific examination and cannot be labelled a fake

CAMERA PRESS

Many remarkable sightings and stories of 'Nessie', the huge marine creature said to dwell in the depths of Scotland's Loch Ness, have been recorded since 1933 when a photograph of the 'monster' was first published in a newspaper.

Loch Ness is situated in the Great Glen in Invernessshire. It is the largest area of fresh water in Scotland reaching a depth of 169 metres (754 feet). It is about 24 miles long and approximately one mile wide – the perfect home for a creature which has been estimated to be 12-15 metres (40-50 feet) long!

This picture is forty six years old

POPPERFOTO

46

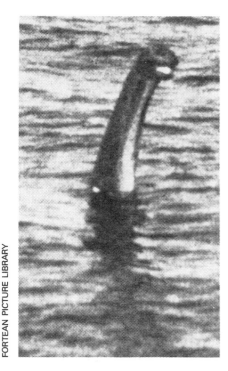

FORTEAN PICTURE LIBRARY

The monster, photographed from Urquhart Castle by Anthony Shiels in May 1977

Many of the films and photographs are immediately dismissed as fakes while others seem to have been genuine sightings. One such photograph was taken in 1955 by Mr P A MacNab. The weather was calm and hazy and like other photos of the 'monster', the picture was taken rather hurriedly. This photograph shows a disturbance of the water very much like the wake created by a passing launch, but evidently this is not so, as the Loch was quite deserted when the picture was taken. To the right is Urquhart Castle, which helps in estimating the size of the monster. Mr MacNab's picture has been expertly examined and tested and has even been through computer analysis. So what is the explanation? Most of Nessie's photographs show a very blurred image of its head and long neck stretching out of the

T DINSDALE

water. Some of these are very convincing indeed!

Recently, after much exploration of the Loch with mini submarines, sonar detection and other scientific equipment, necessary to penetrate the dark and murky loch, there has been an important addition to Nessie's photo album.

In 1972 Dr Robert Rines and a team from the Boston Academy of Applied Science produced some interesting material. As you can see, one of their underwater photographs using sophisticated computerised equipment reveals quite clearly the fin of a very large creature.

In 1975 Dr Rines and his team again achieved a fascinating underwater picture. This one showed the fuzzy outline of a large body and long neck similar in shape to the supposedly extinct Plesiosaurus. This picture is fuzzy because of poor underwater visability. This was made worse by the swell caused by a large mass moving about in the Loch at the time.

Even after all the research, photographic evidence and claims of sightings made by people no one yet knows if there is a 'monster' or even a family of 'monsters' living in Loch Ness.

Dan Taylor from Atlanta USA in his one-man submarine 'Viperfish' at Loch Ness in 1969

Dr Robert Rines released this photograph in 1972 after much research and exploration of the Loch. It is said to be the fin of a very large marine creature resembling the Plesiosaurus of 70 million years ago

ASSOCIATED PRESS LTD

47

A Letter From Norway

Hello! I am a 16-year-old girl from Norway and my name is Monica. I would like to tell you something about myself and Scouting in Norway.

In Norway we learn English at about 12 years of age.

The place in which I live is called Folldal. The village lies at the height of 800 metres above sea level. The population numbers about 2,500 people, most of the local people have farms or they work at the local mine. Our valley lies between big mountains and it is really beautiful here. We have many wild animals living in our forests such as reindeer, elk and musk. Often they get into our gardens and eat our trees. Once a year almost all the men hunt some of these animals. Most of our farmers have cows and sheep, and a few have horses.

It is Autumn now and nearly winter, being the end of October. It is cold at night—15° Centigrade but although we have had snow showers, the deep snow has not yet arrived. Everything is turning brown, the trees and the grass, but there is a special beauty, because it is freezing everything is white with frost and the clear sky is full of the most beautiful stars.

Most Norwegian families have a weekend hut, which is also used in the holidays. Some huts are made of stone and some of wood, usually high in the mountains or beside lakes. These huts are built up high from the ground but in winter, sometimes you have to dig away the snow it is so deep. In summer it is possible to drive a car fairly close but in winter it takes $1\frac{1}{2}$ hours from the car park on cross-country skis to reach the hut. We all carry rucksacks with our food and equipment inside, you must not forget anything!

There is only one school here in Folldal, and you have to go there for 9 years, it is compulsory. If you want to continue with more schooling you have to move to another town far from here. I am going on to the 'gymnasium', it is what you call a high school.

Now to tell you about Scouting. I have been a Scout for 11 years so I have some experience.

We are about 40 Scouts here in Folldal, both girls and boys. We work together in the same group because our Associations, Guides and Scouts, merged in 1978. We now have two Associations, the one I belong to—Norges Speiderforbund (The Norwegian Guide and Scout Association) and another called the Norges KFUK Speidere (Y.W.C.A. Guides of Norway). We are Scouts in my Association from the age 8 years to 18 years. Our Troops are divided into 4 groups and sections:

1st Group:

Boys and girls aged 8-10 years. They have weekly meets. They start their meetings with a Scout-Song. Usually they work together making different sorts of things. For example: They sew pillows which they bring with them when they go on an outing. They are marvellous to sit on when it is cold. Almost every Norwegian Scout has got one. At this time of year, often they make presents for their parents and other people. Christmas cards and Christmas gifts. In Spring they pick birch-branches and give them to old people who live alone. They also make pictures of different sorts of materials perhaps cones, straws and moss.

In Summer they have excursions, they learn to recognise different birds, flowers and animals. In Winter they go ski-ing and sliding, and have great fun. They really enjoy it, mostly playing games and having fun, less of the more serious things.

2nd Group:

These Scouts are at the age of 10-11 years. They have weekly meetings and during this one year they learn much more about Scouting because they are going to join the older Scouts, but still a great deal of time is spent on fun.

3rd Group:

This is for Scouts aged 12-15 years. In Norway we call them "Stifinnere", they learn about the Scouting rules, knots and first aid at some of their meetings which are weekly. They start the meeting with a

M Dunn

Guides-own. One of the girls or boys reads from the New Testament, then one reads a small poem or something similar, and at the end they sing a hymn.

During the meetings they also have courses of different kinds. They finish their meetings with the Scout prayer. Often they have hikes, summer and winter, and stay out for quite a long time. Some go canoeing, and in Norway we usually have the Canadian type of canoe—two people paddle them, one at each end of the boat. It is possible to go canoe camping, carefully packing your equipment into the canoe and tying it inside. Life-jackets must be worn for safety. They may go canoeing around a lake and set up camp not far from the bank at an approved place.

In winter they go ski-ing and dig snow-caves in which they have to spend some nights. In the mountains they have their

Above left: a holiday hut in the mountains

Above right: packing away equipment in preparation for a canoe camping expedition

Below: two of the large, hairy musks that can be seen roaming the frozen countryside

own two small stone huts which they often use. Every summer they meet many other Scouts at camps.

4th Group: (Rangere)

This group is excellent but very small. There are only two groups, Gerd, the other Ranger, takes care of the second group as their Leader. I am very busy and seldom have time to join them because I live in another village, but as often as I can, I attend, I do my best. We help the Leaders at camps.

We have a Scout magazine called "Speideren", and it has lots of interesting things in it. Of course it is all written in Norwegian and you may not understand it. You can imagine my problems to translate Norwegian into English. I hope you were interested in hearing about my Scouting and life in Norway. It is fun to learn about other people, their home, customs and way of life. Goodbye for now, Monica

Next Step

DO YOU REALISE I SHALL BE 14 NEXT MONTH. I SUPPOSE I SHALL HAVE TO LEAVE GUIDES SOON...

WHAT ARE YOU GOING TO DO, JANE?

WILL YOU GO TO RANGERS?

THE RANGER UNIT DOWN THE ROAD DOES SOME GREAT ACTIVITIES I SHALL JOIN WHEN I REACH 14 NEXT YEAR.

Could this be you? Are you wondering what to do when you reach 14 and have completed the Guide programme? One of the possibilities is to become a Ranger. How much do you know about Rangers? Do you know, for instance:

* that you can remain a Ranger until you are 18?

* that there are two types of Unit? One for girls only and one in which a Ranger Guide Unit and a Venture Scout Unit have combined to form a Joint Unit. In a Joint Unit, while following an interesting programme together, each member works for the certificates and badges of his/her section.

* that there are no patrols in a Ranger Unit or a Joint Unit? The members work together in interest groups, for instance car maintenance or flower arranging. At yet another time the whole Unit might work together on a service project.

* that instead of the Patrol Leaders' Council, the Unit is governed by either the Unit in Council, which is the whole Unit—usually a small one—under the chairmanship of one of the members, making plans and carrying them out together; or, if the Unit is larger, by an Executive committee. The members of the Unit elect representatives to form an Executive committee, which in turn elects its own Chairman, Secretary, Treasurer etc. The Leaders work through the Chairman and the Executive committee, so the Unit is self-governing and self-programming and really belongs to the members.

* that before your investiture (Promise Ceremony) you have to complete an Eight Point Challenge? This can take as long as you like—no one will rush you. The Ranger Promise is the same as the Guide Promise but has an extra clause added to it. The Ranger leader asks: 'What is your further responsibility as a Ranger?' and the Ranger answers: 'To be of service to the community.' You re-make your Promise, which includes service to the community, when you feel you are ready to make it in a more adult way and with more adult understanding. It may be the last time you make it, although you may renew it from time to time, so don't rush into it, it needs thinking about.

* that you can work for Interest and Service Certificates if you wish? They are like Guide badges, but more advanced.

These cloth badges show how many Interest Certificates you have gained. Unlike Guide badges, you wear only one at a time, changing them as you gain further certificates.

These metal Service Stars show how many Service Certificates

Rangers?

you have gained. Again, you wear only one at a time, changing them as before until you have four, then you wear the one with the trefoil at the centre.

As with Guide service badges, the service certificates demand that you reach a standard of knowledge and proficiency, because they are concerned with the saving of or maintaining life. In some cases you can gain the certificate of another organisation such as the Red Cross or Royal Life Saving Society etc., which qualifies you to gain the equivalent Ranger Service Certificate.

* that you can gain both Interest and Service Certificates before you make your Promise, and the achievement of qualifying for these could be counted towards your Pre-Investiture Challenge.

* that you can work for the Ranger Challenge, once you are invested? For this you choose a Challenge under each of the Eight Points. If the Unit Executive committee approve of your choice you work through them. As you complete each one you submit a report to the Executive committee. If the members feel you have done sufficiently well you mark it off on your record card. When you have finally achieved all eight you are eligible to receive the metal Ranger Challenge Badge and a certificate signed by the Commonwealth Chief Commissioner.

* that you can also work on the Duke of Edinburgh Award Scheme? Many Rangers do this alongside the general programme of the Unit.

The Unit programme is very flexible and in one group of Rangers learning about interior decorating for example, there might be one working on the Design For Living section of the Duke of Edinburgh scheme, another working for an Interest Certificate, while yet a third is working towards her Ranger Challenge. This doesn't matter at all. What is important is that each one is learning the give and take of working with other people and is making a real effort to improve her knowledge and make progress on the subject.

* that you may choose to do the Young Leader's Scheme as part of the Ranger programme? This scheme gives you the opportunity to work with Brownies or Guides and through doing so experience and learn about leadership. It is quite a demanding scheme but one that is very interesting and satisfying. You are linked with other Young Leaders through the County Leadership Adviser who arranges occasional meetings where you can share your experiences and gain ideas from each other. Your District Commissioner and a Division Leadership Representative can also help you to get as much experience as possible and make sure that you have fun at the same time.

* that you can also gain camping and boating qualifications? Some units spend a lot of time on – and in – the water and have a boating bias and their own boats. Other units do a lot of outdoor activities which require you to learn about lightweight camping because you have to carry your home on your back!

* that you may decide to take part in all the activities of the Unit but not actually work for any badge or certificate? What matters is that you have fun and through working with others come to understand in a more adult way what Guiding is all about.

The Ranger section is for young adults and covers the whole range of adult interests, so 'the choice is yours', and you will receive a very warm welcome to your Ranger Unit.

● *Photographs by H Oleksiuk*

CANAL CRUISING

Going off on a canal boat for a week or two must be almost everyone's idea of a really relaxing holiday – 'getting away from it all' and generally just lazing around.

Life on the canals wasn't always as peaceful however. Around the end of the 18th century, when canals were at their peak of popularity and usefulness, families lived, ate and slept on their boats all year round, usually in very cramped conditions and with very little money to spare.

Canal boats really 'came into their own' as a method of transporting goods and people at the beginning of the 19th century. They could take much bigger loads than a horse and cart, and provided a much more comfortable – albeit slower – means of transport for travellers. The working boats carried goods of every kind, from coal to chocolate, all over Britain.

Before motor-driven boats were invented, they were usually pulled by a pair of horses, walking slowly along the canal bank, one on each side, pulling the boat behind them by means of strong ropes. This sounds like torture for the poor horses, but these were no ordinary animals such as you might find in a riding stables today! They were huge shire horses – very similar to Clydesdales – massive, slow moving beasts capable of pulling tons in weight.

The 'narrow boats' which

Above: this canal boat has had glass windows inserted and is used for pleasure trips
Below: note the beautifully decorated water cans and mop handle

they pulled were often extremely long, depending on how much cargo they normally carried, but, as the name implies, were made very narrow for economy.

The interesting thing about these boats is that, although they are used more for business than pleasure nowadays, the unique style of decorating them has hardly changed at all in over 100 years. Originally, when they were used as floating homes for the workers and their families, the men painted the boats in a very personal style, to make their own stand out from the rest, just as nowadays people paint their doors and windows a different colour from their neighbour.

Typical designs included roses, castles and a side panel with the owner's name and address painted in the famous shaded lettering. Everything possible was decorated – the chimney pots, the water buckets – even the horses had coloured harness beads and were fed from decorated food bowls!

All the boats had names, of course. Girls' names were popular, as were flowers – there were *Violets*, *Marigolds* and *Lilies* in abundance. Sometimes the owner would give away something of his character in his choice of name – boats called *Independence*, *Perseverance* and *Live And Let Live!* were not uncommon.

The inside of the boat was generally just as interesting as the outside – the people may have been poor, but the wives took just as much pride in their floating homes as they would a house on dry land. Everything was compact and multi purpose, from the beds which folded into sofas, to the stove

Taking a holiday on a narrow boat has become very popular

for heating and cooking. Not so very different from caravans today, in fact! Victorian 'boat-wives' were very fond of fancy decorations, and every spare inch of space was covered with pictures, tapestries, embroidered mats and decorated plates.

Canals were really a way of life for these people – there was even a school for the children on board an old barge on the Grand Union Canal!

Sadly, with the advent of the railways around 1850, trade on the canals began to die out. Trains were faster, and just as comfortable for passengers than canal boats – if not more so – and, in the long run, far less expensive (in 1830, the Caledonian Canal in Scotland was completed – at a cost of £980,000!). As the narrow-boat trade declined, families began to move away to find jobs on dry land, and the whole tradition began to look as if it would disappear completely.

Luckily, however, there were still some canal enthusiasts who refused to let this happen, and they continued to live on

the boats and make a living as best they could from them. And nowadays canals are becoming popular all over again – this time with holiday makers. Over 2 million people took to the water last year and canal holidays are gaining attraction all the time. On the Norfolk Broads in summertime there were often queues to get through the locks! Cabin Cruisers, with their own motors, make life afloat streamlined and easy.

We took these photographs near Leighton Buzzard in Bedfordshire. You can see how busy the canal is – working boats, 'cruisers' taking passengers on day trips, and 'second homes' all sharing the water. Notice how beautifully and painstakingly the boats have been decorated – it's nice to know, isn't it, that the craft is still continuing?

If you're interested in finding out more about canals and narrow boats, by far the best place to go is the British Waterways Museum at Stoke Bruerne, Northants. It's a mine of information on the subject, and even has a shop full of souvenirs.

Hands Up!

. . . anyone who would like to be able to look into the future! Yes, we thought so—everyone likes to think that there *is* a way of foretelling what will happen next week or next year—be it by reading tea leaves, interpreting dreams or gazing into a crystal ball!

Have you ever looked closely at your hands? No? Well, now is the time to discover what they could be telling you about yourself. Take a close look at the palms of your hands and you will see that there are many lines and creases running in all directions.

So here, just for fun, is our guide to palmistry. We can't guarantee that it's an accurate way of forecasting, but it is interesting and quite a lot of fun, too!

There are three main lines on the palm of the hand—the Life line, the Head line and the Heart line. The idea is that by studying the different shapes and sizes of these lines, you can tell someone's character. Better start on your own before you make any wild guesses!

The LIFE LINE curves down from under the thumb and controls health and energy.

1. Long and clearly marked—good health and vitality.

2. Crosses mean small worries, but you should be able to overcome them without difficulty.

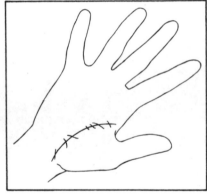

3. Sloping towards the centre of the hand?—you will travel a lot.

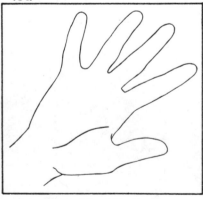

4. A break in the Life line means a sudden change in your life. If the break is near the top of

the hand, this will be in early life, if towards the centre, in middle age, and so on.

5. A double line signifies a very lucky life indeed—you'll be very healthy.

The HEAD LINE reveals your career prospects. It's the one leading up from your wrist towards your fingers.

6. Line leading up towards the little finger—a career involving lots of communication with others seems likely.

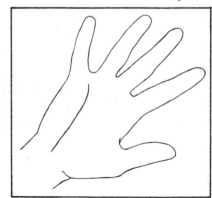

7. Relatives will play a big part in your career choice if your head line starts on the thumb pad.

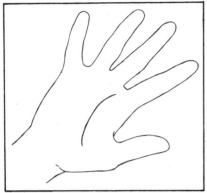

8. Going up towards the ring finger? Any artistic career will prove very successful for you.

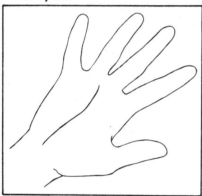

9. If the line stretches to the index finger, your career will put you in authority over others.

10. A broken head line, or one with a 'branch', as depicted in the illustration, means that a romance will prob-

ably influence your career – it may not be your own romance, however!

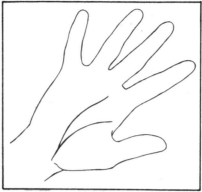

The HEART LINE runs across the top of the hand below the fingers. It governs your emotion.

11. Heart line starting under middle finger – you are both sensible and cheerful, and are very good company.

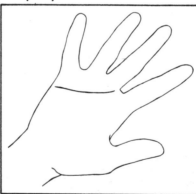

12. Fairly long and curved line – you are a warm and friendly person.

13. Starting high up under index finger – you are outgoing, confident and very ambitious.

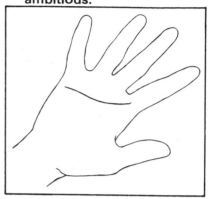

14. A wavy, erratic line – you change your mind every two minutes!

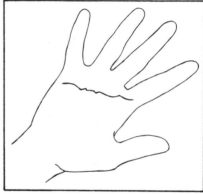

15. A very short line – your head always rules your heart.

What have you been able to reveal about yourself? Are you going to travel, be lucky and cheerful? Whatever your conclusion, don't take it too seriously.

Brighten up your pull-on hat with a couple of pom-poms or a multi-coloured tassel or plait a fake plait with several different colours and textures of wool!

Bla
thic
in a
an

a
j

Plait several lengths of coloured wool 1m. long and wear it as a belt!

Sew shiny ball buttons and strips of black braid onto a red jumper. Wear it with a shiny black belt for a military look!

cutting line

30cm

Cut the neckline of a black jumper to a wide 'V'. Bind it with silver braid and sew on diamanté for a smashing party top!

Cut the sleeves off a jumper and cut down from the shoulder 30cm. (see diag.) Bind the edges with coloured braid and you have a slip-over.

Po
elbows
tomate

Cut a big jumper down the front and sew in a big zip to make a bomber jacket. Cut a slit either side and bind each slit with tartan ribbon to make fake pockets. Add tartan armbands!

Sew little ribbon bo
all over a j
tie a couple
ribbons o
hair-grips a
wear those to

ool Done!...

Brighten up your winter clothes with ribbons and fringing, appliqués and buttons, embroidery and bindings, jewels and patches!

titch a
ed wool
sting colour
e edges
leeve-less
un.
t over
-stitched

Sew fringing down the arms and side of a jumper — wear it with a 'kerchief for a cowboy look!

Make multi-coloured tassels and knot them onto a plain scarf!

Cut a simple tie, handkerchief and buttons out of felt and sew them onto a plain jumper! Add a diamanté stick pin!

Buy two jewelled or sequinned motifs and sew one either side of your jumper.

Cut two jumpers in exactly the same place — stick a strip of sellotape where you intend to cut first so that the knitting won't fray — and re-sew them to make two much more eye-catching ones!

Do some embroidery on your woollen gloves — simple chain stitch looks fine!

TESTS IN THE DARK

One of the aims of Guiding is to train you to work under adverse conditions, and this includes being able to do things satisfactorily in the dark. There is no substitute, of course, for going out on night hikes, tracking and playing wide games at all sorts of creepy hours, but you can get in some good practice and have lots of fun, too, merely by switching off the lights in the Guide hall. Some of the ideas suggested here can be done with your Patrol, others are better if the whole Company takes part.

What about that routine for falling in the Patrols for inspection? Try doing it in the dark. And can you tie knots – with the lights out?

Don't Get Lost

Much the same points apply to map and compass work. For really keen Guides, getting lost out of doors is an occupational hazard. A little practice beforehand in the Guide hall will stand you in good stead when it comes to finding your way by compass and map in the dark.

Ear and Touch Detection

As a Guide you will, or should have, a reputation for your excellent powers of observation. We often overlook the fact, however, that we have other senses as well as sight. Put out the lights and find out who can locate a hidden watch 'by ear'. Lay a trail on the floor, using matchsticks to make the woodcraft signs, and follow it by touch.

You could also test the Company's sense of taste in the dark. Blindfold someone and give her a taste of an ordinary food, on a teaspoon. You'll be surprised at the unlikely suggestions they produce for the name of the food! When you go to camp, you could have a competition when everyone is having supper round the camp fire!

Lights Up!

Now here are two games which are always popular when played in our Company. For the first you will need a mat, or, better still, a number of mats of different sizes. The mat is placed on the floor and everyone gathers at the opposite end of the room. When the lights are switched out and the whistle blown, everyone tries to get on the mat. After a few seconds the lights are switched on again, and anyone who is not on the mat is 'out'. As the game progresses the mat can be replaced by a smaller one. Try shifting the mat to a different part of the floor or removing it altogether after the lights go out – but before the whistle is blown!

Shoes In The Dark

The second game can also produce some hilarious results. It is best played as an inter-Patrol game. Everyone has to take off her shoes and place them in a heap in the middle of the room. Then the Patrols form up, roughly equidistant to the centre of the floor. Everyone tries to fit herself out with a pair of shoes – any pair. The lights are then switched on again and the Patrol scores are counted up. Award ten points for each pair of matching shoes on the correct feet. Give five for a pair of matching shoes on the wrong feet or a pair which do not match but which are on the correct feet. Subtract two points for each shoeless foot.

Now try to think up your own games to play in the dark! Remember all the games and stunts you have had on your Company programme and see how many of them can be adapted for playing in the dark. Have fun!

Just The Job

Choosing a career needn't be a problem any more – we've done all the hard work for you! Answer our quiz honestly, and we'll match your personality to a suitable job. Simple, isn't it? But it's just for fun – don't take it *too* seriously! Start by answering these general questions:

1. You're given a book token as a birthday present. Would you be most likely to buy:
A. *A book about animals*
B. *A book on travel or adventure*
C. *A study textbook*
D. *A novel you've heard recommended?*

2. You're shopping with a friend, and she wants to buy a dress which does nothing for her. Would you:
A. *Tell her so, tactfully*
B. *Think the final choice is up to her and refuse to interfere*
C. *Drop large hints about another one suiting her more*

D. *Feel too scared to tell her what you think?*

3. On a long train journey, would you:
A. *Chat to your neighbours*
B. *Take along a selection of magazines to read*
C. *Study some homework or read a schoolbook*
D. *Feel embarrassed and look out of the window rather than at the other passengers?*

4. If you could choose any form of transport at all, would you pick:
A. *A motorbike*
B. *A snazzy sports car*
C. *A Rolls-Royce*
D. *A helicopter?*

5. Which of these colours is your favourite:
A. *Green*
B. *Red*
C. *Brown*
D. *Blue?*

Now then! Work out which letter you have most of, then go on to one of the next sections as follows: Mostly A's, go on to section A, Mostly B's, go to section B, and so on.

SECTION A

1. If you came on to the scene of a road accident, what would you do?
A. *Ring for an ambulance*
B. *Rush up to help in any way you could*
C. *Try to keep any children away from the scene*
D. *Stand helplessly, thinking it would be better not to interfere?*

2. Out for a walk in the country, it starts to rain. What would you do?
A. *Put on your kagoul, which you were of course carrying with you*

B. *Run for cover under the nearest tree*
C. *Worry about what your Mum will say when you come home drenched*
D. *Accept that you're going to get wet anyway, and enjoy it?*

3. You find a stray dog running around in the road. Would you:
A. *Take it home and hope that no one claims it so that you can keep it*

B. *Look for its name disc and take it to its owners*
C. *Not be quite sure whether to approach it at all*
D. *Take it to the nearest police station?*

4. Travelling in a rather crowded lift, it suddenly stops between floors. Would you:
A. *Tell yourself not to panic*
B. *Start thinking about other things to keep your mind off the situation*
C. *Try to calm everyone else down*
D. *Get impatient over the waste of time?*

5. You wake up in the middle of the night and hear a noise downstairs. Would you:
A. *Shout 'Go get him, Rover',*
even if you don't have a dog
B. *Go back to sleep*
C. *Lie awake all night, trembling*
D. *Run through to your parents' room and wake them up?*
Now find out which letter you have most of. Mostly A—your key number is 1. Mostly B—your key number is 2. Mostly C—your key number is 3. Mostly D—your key number is 4. Turn to page 77 to find just the job for you!

SECTION B
1. You have to write a thank you letter to your aunt, for a present you don't really like. Would you:
A. *Start a letter half a dozen times but never finish it*
B. *Keep putting it off*
C. *Write a nice letter straight away, to get it over with*
D. *Write, but find it difficult to sound pleased?*

2. You can't decide which to buy—a useful raincoat or a party dress. You can't afford both. Would you finally decide to:
A. *Take the raincoat, but keep wishing you had bought the dress instead*
B. *Spend so long making up your mind they're both sold*
C. *Take the raincoat, but decide to save up for the dress*
D. *Pick the dress—of course?*

3. Mum says you can stay up late on Saturday if you do the washing up (which you hate) all week. Do you:
A. *Agree, reluctantly*
B. *Agree, but 'forget' half way through the week*
C. *Bribe your little brother to do it for you*
D. *Ask if you can do something else instead?*

4. You audition for, and are given a part in the school play. Do you think:
A. *Good—maybe a passing producer will discover me*
B. *Help—I wonder if they'll let me resign*
C. *I hope the rehearsals won't take up too much of my time*
D. *Terriffic—I can't wait?*

5. Imagine you've won a competition prize of a holiday anywhere in the world. Would you choose to go to:
A. *Europe*
B. *A secluded South Sea island*
C. *Africa*
D. *America?*

Which letter appears most in your answers? If it's A, your key number is 5; B—your key number is 6; C—your key number is 7; D—your key number is 8. The job for you is on page 77!

SECTION C
1. Three days before your birthday, a parcel arrives in the post. Would you:
A. *Keep it, unopened, until your birthday*
B. *Open it up, 'just for a quick look'*
C. *Try hard to resist, but end up opening it on the day before your birthday*
D. *Tell Mum to hide it until your birthday?*

2. A friend tells you a 'secret', although you don't really think it would matter if everyone knew. So would you:
A. Just tell your best friend
B. Tell someone you know to be a chatterbox, so she will be blamed
C. Tell everyone you know
D. Not tell a soul?

3. How would you spend an evening at home on your own:
A. Washing your hair and catching up on all the little chores that need doing
B. Watching TV and/or reading

C. 'Phoning all your friends
D. Doing some extra home-work?

4. Which of these ways of 'foretelling the future' would you be most likely to believe in:
A. Reading your horoscope in a magazine
B. Madame Zaza and her crys-tal ball
C. Palm reading (if so, turn to page 54!)
D. None of them — they're all nonsense?

5. About half of the class — in-cluding you — start to talk when the teacher leaves the room. When she returns, she asks the chatterers to stand up. Do you:

A. Wait for other people to move first, then stand up
B. Sit still and keep your fingers crossed
C. Look so guilty and red faced that you have to stand up
D. Stand up immediately?
Which letter have you written most often? A — your key number is 9; B — your key number is 10; C — your key number is 11; D — your key number is 12. Now turn to page 77, where you'll find just the job for you!

SECTION D

1. You see an old lady standing at a zebra crossing, looking worried. Would you:
A. Rush over and take her across the road
B. Stand there wondering if she really needs help or not
C. Go up to her and ask politely if she needs help
D. Walk on?

2. A well known politician comes to speak at your school. Would you:
A. Listen carefully to his talk and tell your parents about it afterwards
B. Go along, but find yourself falling asleep half way through
C. Ask him some relevant ques-tions afterwards
D. Not bother to go?

3. Is your schoolbag:
A. Neat and tidy, with pencils sharpened and books covered
B. As full of library books as it is of schoolbooks
C. Usually quite empty — you only take the books you need at any time
D. So full of sweet papers there's no room for books?

4. You're waiting for a lift to go up seven floors. When it arrives, it's already crowded. Would you:
A. Ask everyone politely to move inside a bit
B. Wait for the next one
C. Decide to walk instead
D: Push people out of the way to get in, standing on their feet if necessary?

5. Out shopping for the day in a busy city, you somehow man-age to get lost. Do you:
A. Consult the town map, which you are carrying
B. Panic
C. Look for a policeman
D. Keep on walking?

Count up your scores. The letter which appears most often gives your key number. A is 13, B is 14, C is 15, D is 16. You'll find just the job for you on page 77.

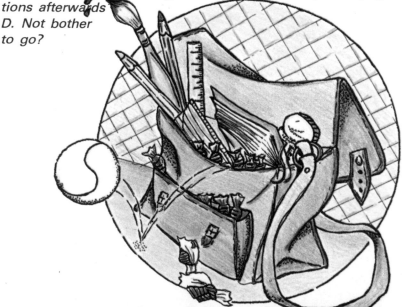

Guides' Own

NIGHT IN THE WOODS

The hoot of an owl sent a chill down my spine,
As I stood in the shadow of the oak and the pine.
Darkness had fallen, the sunlight had gone,
I felt for my torch and then turned it on.
A small yellow glow in the dark dreary night,
A squirrel crept out and gave me a fright.

The fox on the prowl cried out loud, harsh and clear,
The feel of a hand made me quiver with fear.
I took a sharp turn and made a sound,
Was it the fox or a twig on the ground?
The hand I had felt was only a tree,
A dead hanging branch, but it frightened me.

Judith Lewis, 1st Argoed (Wales) Coy.

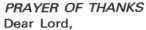

PRAYER OF THANKS

Dear Lord,

We thank you for the birds, the trees, the lakes and especially for Mother Nature. Thank you for giving us sight to see these pretty things. Bless those who can't see these things. Sometimes we take seeing for granted but we should be eternally grateful.
In your name, Amen.

Heather Lawrence, 5th Dunfermline Coy.

CAT FIGHT

Eyes meet through grass,
A growling tone rings out.
Creeping slowly on all four paws,
Within them are the sharpest claws.

Hair rising, neck and tail,
Each thinking, must not fail.
Back arched, eyes flashing,
Limbs stiff, tail lashing.

Closer, closer, growling louder,
A pause, then a hiss,
Both spring and attack,
A paw lashes out, just missing a back.

Claws scratching, teeth biting,
One is weak, no strength for fighting.
Eyes wild, he runs, unhurt.
The other stands proud, but alert.

Lorna Bartley, 45th Totley
(Sheffield) Coy.

PATROL PUZZLE

How many Guide Badges can you find hidden in this puzzle?
Answer on page 77

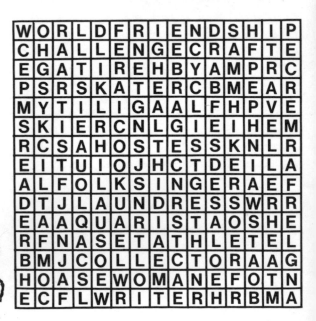

W	O	R	L	D	F	R	I	E	N	D	S	H	I	P
C	H	A	L	L	E	N	G	E	C	R	A	F	T	E
E	G	A	T	I	R	E	H	B	Y	A	M	P	R	C
P	S	R	S	K	A	T	E	R	C	B	M	E	A	R
M	Y	T	I	L	I	G	A	A	L	F	H	P	V	E
S	K	I	E	R	C	N	L	G	I	E	I	H	E	M
R	C	S	A	H	O	S	T	E	S	S	K	N	L	R
E	I	T	U	I	O	J	H	C	T	D	E	I	L	A
A	L	F	O	L	K	S	I	N	G	E	R	A	E	F
D	T	J	L	A	U	N	D	R	E	S	S	W	R	R
E	A	A	Q	U	A	R	I	S	T	A	O	S	H	E
R	F	N	A	S	E	T	A	T	H	L	E	T	E	L
B	M	J	C	O	L	L	E	C	T	O	R	A	A	G
H	O	A	S	E	W	O	M	A	N	E	F	O	T	N
E	C	F	L	W	R	I	T	E	R	H	R	B	M	A

Catherine Welch, 1st Cringleford Coy.

Contributions

A VISIT TO 'OUR CHALET'

Recently a group of local Guides went on holiday to Switzerland, the purpose of our visit being to go to 'Our Chalet' in Adelboden. We had to walk up a lot of hills to get there, but it was worth it for the view alone—we could see the whole of Adelboden below us, surrounded by snow capped mountains!

In the chalet, we were shown into a large, pine furnished dining room, where we were told how the chalet was given to the Guides as a present by the wealthy Helen Storrow. After this talk we were shown round the chalet, and saw first of all the library, or 'English Room' as it is known, which is a small room filled with Guiding books such as 'The Guide Annual' and so on. We were then shown the American Room, which had a large patchwork quilt. The quilt was made in large squares, decorated with colourful embroidery worked by American Girl Scouts. After this, we met some foreign Guides with whom we swapped badges.

Outside in the grounds we met Guides from America, Norway and Australia and also a Canadian Commissioner. They were all very friendly, and we swapped more badges!

We all thoroughly enjoyed our visit, and hope to have the chance to go again.

Gillian Robertson, 1st Portbury (Avon) Coy.

SCOUTING IN AMERICA

When my family emigrated to America three years ago I decided that one of the first things I would do would be to join a Girl Scout troop, as I had enjoyed being a Brownie and then a Guide in Great Britain.

I became a member of the Cadette Girl Scout Troop 190, which was connected to the Dwight D. Eisenhower Junior High School, which I attended. During my two years with them I joined in activities as varied as making Valentine's Day place mats for the local Children's Home, to visiting a police station and hearing a court case.

Our main way of fund raising was to go from door to door selling Girl Scout cookies (biscuits) and Girl Scout peanuts.

I camped quite a few times with my troop and council. In America the tents are erected on wooden platforms to protect the campers from snakes and racoons. The British way of camping is known as 'primitive camping' and the American way is certainly more luxurious!

At the end of each year we had a Troop Badge Ceremony in which we were presented with our awards. The highlight for me was when I was awarded with the highest award in Girl Scouting, the First Class Girl Scout award.

After two years in America my family returned to Great Britain. It was an unforgettable experience and I feel I had a real view of the World Association of Girl Guides and Girl Scouts.

Elizabeth Crow, 4th Chester, (St Mary's) Coy.

THE GUIDING HIGHWAY CODE

 —Guider sleeping.

 —Guider putting up tents.

 —Not the ideal place for sleeping!

 —Not the best place to camp!

 —Amount of people allowed on the site.

 —Don't trample on the farmer's field!

 —Putting the tents up the wrong way!

 —Carry your equipment from here on.

 —Don't lean on the tent that way!

Joanne Rankin, Beaconsfield.

Brighten Up Your Room

*Collect attractive, brightly coloured tins and jars (e.g. Marmite, Lyle's golden syrup). Use them to store drawing pins, pens and pencils, rubbers – anything! *Or* paint designs on old, clean jam jars with poster paints.

*Arrange tall grasses in an old cider jar or a jug – Mum or Gran might have an old earthenware jug you could use. You can buy coloured dried grasses in department stores or florists, or simply go out and pick your own – the natural colours often look just as pretty. Or try making huge paper flowers from tissue paper and wire.

*Collect plain glass jam jars, remove the labels and fill ⅔ of the way up with small washed pebbles or shells. Now fill up the jars with water, coloured with a few drops of food dye – a row of blue and green, or pink and purple, jars looks very pretty.

*A long wooden plank resting on two or three bricks at either end makes a super shelf for books or pot plants.

*Keep a big bowl of pot pourri in your room all the time if you want it to smell lovely – fill it with flower petals (rose petals are best, but any strong scented flower will do), sprinkle a little salt and a handful of cloves on the top, and leave in a warm, dry place. Remember to stir the petals round every so often to release the fragrance properly, and add new petals every so often.

*Turn all your posters over and draw you own pictures on the back!

*Lemonade crates, turned upside down and covered with a cloth, make useful small tables.

*A large, strong twig, "anchored" in a small flower pot with Blu-Tack, makes an unusual ring holder.

*Empty food tins, with the labels removed, make startling and effective flower pots. Do be very careful when removing the lids, though.

*Buy a packet of gold gummed paper stars and stick them all round the edge of your dressing table mirror. You too can be a superstar!

Things To Do
*You many not be able to alter your bedclothes at all, but you can cheer up a pillowcase very easily by embroidering a little motif in the corner. Trace the design onto a plain cotton pillowslip with a pen, then, using embroidery silks, sew neatly over the design. Don't try anything too complicated at first, otherwise you might get discouraged. You'll soon get the hang of it, though, and progress on to more elaborate ideas. What about a small flower or a sun to start with? Once you've got the hang of it, you could try embroidering your own name. Do remember to ask Mum's permission first.

*If you've never tried growing anything before, now's the time to start! Even a carrot top in a saucer looks pretty when it starts to shoot green leaves. Mustard and cress are easily grown on damp cotton wool or blotting paper, and you can buy all sorts of indoor herbs and plants from nurseries and garden shops. All you need is a sunny windowsill and a little patience! Experiment with fruit seeds – orange and lemon pips, apple seeds and so on. Avocado pear stones turn into quite spectacular plants if you look after them properly in the early stages. Even if you think you don't have green fingers at all, you can still keep a row of cacti plants on a shelf – leave them alone and they'll look after themselves!

*Frame an old fashioned mirror with a piece of lace or lace-type fabric. If your bedroom already has a Victorian look, complete the theme by making little mats, with a frill round the edge, for your dressing table.

*Fill an old coffee jar with a 'bouquet' of feather dusters!

*Stick a single row of mirror tiles down the inside of your wardrobe door for a very effective full length mirror.

*If there is an old deckchair in the garage, try and persuade Dad to part with it. Paint the wooden parts with gloss paint (red or white would look especially nice), tie two big cushions onto the seat and back and hey presto! A new armchair for your room!

*Stick a few rubber suction teatowel holders along the back

of the door and hang scarves in them.

*Replace your light bulb with a coloured one—this simple move can make all the difference to a room, completely changing its character according to the colour of the bulb you use. Try pink or apricot for a warm, pretty glow, lilac for a feminine, Victorian look, or experiment with green, blue, orange or red for a *really* different look!

Things To Make

*Turn your bed into a daytime sofa simply by adding a few cushions. They're easy and cheap to make—Mum will probably have lots of spare pieces of material, but if not 'oddments' can be bought very cheaply. Choose materials to match your colourscheme (dye with 'Dylon' fabric dye first if necessary), sew up three sides, stuff the cushion with foam chips, old tights or cushion pads and sew up the fourth side (or use a zip or Velcro if you want to be able to take the cushion cover off to wash). If you have all of your materials ready, you can easily make up several cushions in an evening. Now comes the fun part—decorating the front of the cushion. Use your imagination here—trace your name in felt tip pen for a guide-line, and sew over it, embroider your Zodiac sign, or simply sew on a random pattern of sequins for a very bright and cheerful look. The cushions can be made as big or as small as you like— what about making some really huge floor cushions for your friends to sit on when they come round? Or what about making a really novel cushion from an old T-shirt?

*Make a mobile! You will need some strong cardboard, glue and decorations in the way of felt tip pens, coloured tin foil, tiny feathers etc., etc. Cut out your basic shape—keep this simple, like a flower or bird outline—and use it as a template to cut out three other shapes. Colour them in with felt tips (on both sides, remember!) and decorate with strips of coloured foil or anything else which comes to mind (nothing too heavy, though, or the mobile will not hang properly). Sew strong thread through the shapes and attach them to two crossed drinking straws (see diagram). Hang the mobile carefully from a strong piece of coloured string attached to the ceiling with Blu-Tack. Keep the mobile away from strong draughts, or it will fall down every time the wind blows!

*If your room is about to be repainted anyway, ask your parents if you can paint a giant mural on one wall. How lovely to wake up on a deserted South Sea island every morning!

Things To Buy

*Buy a plastic shoe tidy with several pockets, to keep all your bits and pieces in. Excellent for keeping hairbrushes, shampoo bottles, socks, handkerchiefs —oh, yes—and shoes!

*Small wicker work fruit bowls are very cheap and look really pretty on a dressing table, filled with odds and ends of jewellery, hair slides etc.

*Buy a plastic cutlery tray from Woolworths and use it to keep small bottles, hair grips, buttons and so on from getting lost.

*Buy half a dozen plastic windmills from a toy shop, place them in a jam jar on the windowsill and watch them blow in the breeze.

*Make a collection of tiny pictures and hang them vertically in a row on a piece of black velvet ribbon—very Victorian!

*Buy a piece of hardboard, ask Dad to drill a hole in the top and hang it up in your room. Use it as a memo board and keep track of dentist's appointments, books you want to read, birthdays to remember—and as a showpiece for postcards, drawings, badges and so on. You'll soon wonder how you ever managed without it! If you want your board to look really good you can cover the hardboard with cork tiles before adding the notices.

Problems and Puzzles

Campsite Problem

There are four Patrol camps in this field. The Patrols have decided to share the field equally. Each Patrol must have a sleeping tent, a store tent, a fire, and a lat. Can you work out the camp boundaries according to instructions?

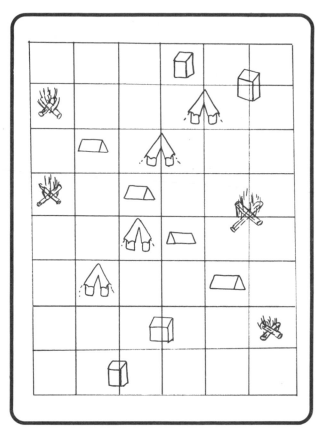

Camping Crossword

How much do you know about camping? Find out by starting at number one, and working your way round the spiral. The last letter of each answer is the first letter of the next.

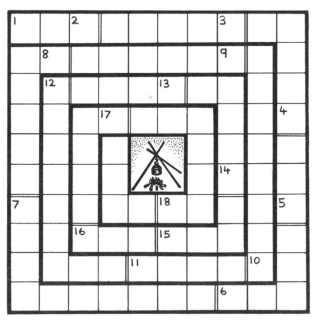

Clues

1. To get you where you're going (3)
2. Type of pressure stove (6)
3. In which a knife or an axe should be kept when not in use (6)
4. Handle of an axe (4)
5. Kindling (6)
6. Guy rope should be at this to back of peg (11)
7. Type of bush-saw (7)
8. Helps you to find your way (7)
9. Cooking in water below boiling-point (9)
10. The kind of stick to cook sausages on (5)
11. A poisonous plant said to be deadly (10)
12. Wood to avoid for burning—it gives off thick smoke (5)
13. Type of pack (6)
14. Drinking water should be this (5)
15. Grease axe-heads and saw-blades to prevent this (4)
16. B.-P. said that nothing except these should be left behind at a site (6)
17. Preparing to leave camp (8)
18. Type of fire in which pot hangs from a tripod (see illustration) (5)

Projects in Summer

If you go on a long journey keep a note of the different birds you see.

Kestrel

Lapwing

Many birds seem to be unafraid of cars.

Pheasant

If you go to the coast look at the different ways in which birds feed.

Try to discover what the birds are feeding on by digging in the sand. See 'Wader Feeding' on page 39.

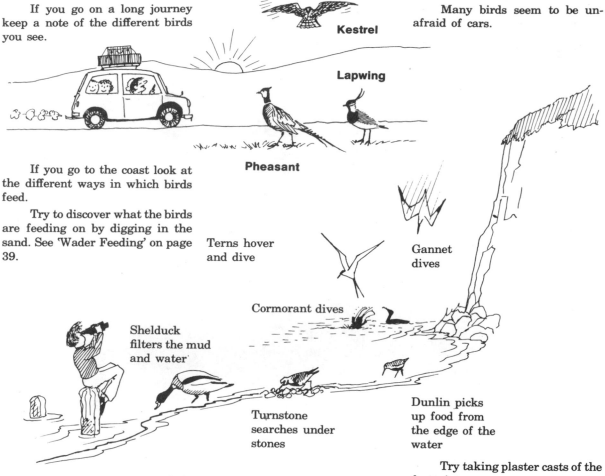

Terns hover and dive

Gannet dives

Cormorant dives

Shelduck filters the mud and water

Turnstone searches under stones

Dunlin picks up food from the edge of the water

Try taking plaster casts of the footprints.

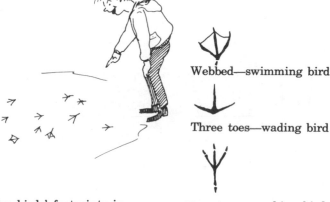

Webbed—swimming bird

Three toes—wading bird

Four toes—perching bird

Look for birds' footprints in the sand and mud.

CARDBOARD RING ROUND FOOTPRINT

Pour in plaster of Paris.

Wait until dry, remove plaster and brush off any soil. Full details are available from YOC, The Lodge, Sandy, Bedfordshire, SG19 2DL.

and Autumn

Put up a bird table in your garden. Look to see what birds are attracted to it.

A bird table can be made from an old tray and hung from a branch of a tree. Put out kitchen scraps or specially bought bird food.

Autumn is the time to clean out your nestboxes. Take out the old nest and see what material was used, then wash out the box.

Look out for flocks of birds going to roost. Often birds use regular flight lines. Trace these lines on a map and discover where the birds roost. Rooks and starlings are good species to study.

Look for pellets, especially those of owls or other birds of prey. By dissecting a pellet you can identify the undigested parts of the bird's food and discover what it has eaten.

Pull pellet apart using tweezers and a straightened-out paper clip.

Soak in water to soften the pellet, then mount the bones and fur on a card.

Barn Owl
Offord · 2 · 11 · 76

skulls

hind legs

ribs

back bones

fur

teeth

Projects in Winter

The beginning of a new year is an ideal time to start keeping a notebook.

If you cannot recognise a bird write down a description and make a note of any obvious markings on a simple diagram.

2 January – MARCH END.
Cold Sunny – no wind.
10.30 – 12.00.
Heron flew west mobbed by black headed gulls
Tufted duck 2♂ 2♀ swimming and diving on lake – one bird stayed under for 20 seconds.

Black
White collar
Brown
Sparrow sized –
in reeds on edge of lake
White in tail
Probably ♂
reed bunting

Remember to jot down what the birds are doing.

How to build a nestbox

Winter is the best time to make nestboxes. You should have them finished and in position by the end of March. Instructions of how to build a nestbox are available from YOC, The Lodge, Sandy, Bedfordshire, SG19 2DL.

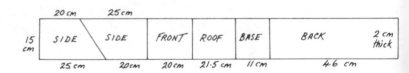

	20 cm	25 cm					
15 cm	SIDE	SIDE	FRONT	ROOF	BASE	BACK	2 cm thick
	25 cm	20 cm	20 cm	21.5 cm	11 cm	46 cm	

Make a hole 2.9 cm in diameter in the front of the box.

Add the roof using brass hinges or a strip of rubber.

The box must be placed two and a half metres above ground level, facing north or east.

Blue tits and great tits are the birds most likely to use your nestbox...

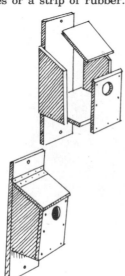

Try to obtain permission to put the boxes up in your school grounds or in the local hospital grounds.

...or house sparrows and starlings if the hole is too large.

and Spring

Now is the time to watch your nestboxes.

Record the day-to-day life of your nesting birds. This will mean sitting down quite a long way from the nest so that the birds do not know that you are watching.

Your notes may look like this:

> Blue tit in nestbox - Offord 1977 (small town garden)
>
> 20 Apr. - started collecting nest material.
> 22 Apr. - both birds collecting moss.
> 26 Apr. - one bird collecting feathers
> 28 Apr - two eggs in box.
> 10. May - eight eggs in box.
> 17. May - parents taking in caterpillars
> 20. May - looked carefully in box and found six young had hatched.
> 5 Jun - Five young blue tits left box.

The birds are busy advertising their territory to attract mates. They are also warning other birds to keep out. See 'Trespassers Beware!' on page 22.

Look out for summer migrants returning from their winter quarters. Keep a note in your diary of the dates on which you first see them. You may also notice flocks of winter visitors moving north to breed.

Skylark

Robin

Wren

Spring is the best time to listen to bird-song.

Sit quietly and try to recognise the birds singing.

You can also learn your bird-song from records and tapes.

The One Night Camp

Suzie White and her twin, Nicky, straightened the sleeping-bags inside their tent. Suzie crawled out through the tent flap. Nicky crawled out under the side walls and nearly brought the tent down on top of her.

"Why don't you use the front door?" asked Suzie, going round the tent to retighten the guy-ropes.

"Good idea!" Nicky crawled back under the side walls, then reappeared out of the tent flap. She grinned and rubbed her hands. "It'll be great fun camping out tonight, Suzie."

"Not if I have to spend all night going round after you," grumbled Suzie, again tightening up the guy-ropes.

While the girls were at the tent, their father, Mr White, uncoiled a roll of double wire from the house to the tent and attached the two bare ends to the terminals on a switchbox.

Mrs White looked on anxiously. "I do hope the twins will be safe staying out all night," she said nervously. "I wouldn't have agreed to it if they hadn't been so pressing."

"They're pressing all right," said Mr White grimly. "They keep on until they wear you out into saying yes."

"There have been a lot of burglaries in the neighbourhood recently," went on Mrs. White. "Apart from breaking into the Guide hall, thieves raided a house in Parkfield and broke into one in Highfield last week."

"The last thing a burglar would want to do, my dear Amelia, is to steal those two girls. If they did they'd wish they hadn't." He reached the tent and poked his head inside.

"Don't forget they did break into the Guide hall," pursued Mrs White. "They stole the Guides' camp money and half of their camping gear."

"I know. It really is very hard luck on the Guides," said Mr White sympathetically. "Fancy having to cancel their camp because of thieves! Yes, the least we can do now is to let our two camp out in the garden tonight —just a one-night camp. They aren't little girls now, you know."

"I hope you're right."

"You worry too much about them, my dear Amelia."

"Yes, don't worry about us, Mum," said Nicky.

"It's only for one night, remember," said Mrs White.

Mr White pressed the button on the switchbox, which rang a bell in the house.

"Come here, twins," he said, beckoning Suzie and Nicky into the tent. "I'll leave this switchbox in here with you. If you should need me in a hurry give one long ring. If you want me to come, but not urgently, give two short rings." He demonstrated what he meant by operating the switchbox.

"And if we don't want you to come we'll give you three rings, shall we, Daddy?" said Nicky.

"Don't ring unnecessarily," said Mr White sternly. "I intend to get some sleep, even if your mother stays awake worrying about you."

"What about making a test signal?" asked Suzie, who was itching to press the button.

"I've already tested it," said Mr White. "The alarm is in perfect working order, and kindly avoid waking me up at two o'clock in the morning." He

72

"What's happened? What's the matter?" he gasped out.

placed the switchbox beside the far tent-pole, in between the two sleeping-bags. He tucked the wire under one of the sleeping-bags and crawled out backwards. "Now, remember, girls, use the switchbox only when you want to call me; otherwise, keep your itchy little fingers off that button. Understand?"

"Yes, Daddy." Nicky pressed the button several times and listened intently.

"What are you doing?" shouted Mr White.

"Just testing, Daddy, but I can't hear the alarm."

"Of course you can't!" cried Mr White. "It rings in the house, not in the tent. It's too far away for you to hear it. Now, if you try any more testing I'll tie you up with the wire. Now kindly get into your pyjamas and let us all get some sleep."

The girls put on their pyjamas, carefully folded up their uniforms, which they had insisted on wearing at "camp", and laid them in a neat pile at the foot of their sleeping-bags.

"The burglars have been round already," said Nicky, looking round the tent. "Somebody's

stolen my hat."

"It's still on your head," Suzie pointed out.

"Gosh, so it is!"

The girls crawled into their sleeping-bags. Mr White looked at them. "Have you got everything you need now?"

"Oh, I've forgotten my cold-water bottle," said Suzie.

"Cold-water bottle? What do you want with a cold-water bottle?"

"I keep my orangeade in it."

"She means this, George," said Mrs White.

Mrs White handed in a water-bottle and two tin mugs. "Goodnight, girls!" she said. "Mind you go to sleep."

"Goodnight!" added Mr White, tying up the tent flap.

"Yippee!" cried Nicky excitedly. She crawled out of her sleeping-bag. "Let's have a drink, Suzie."

Unscrewing the cap of her water-bottle, she poured out two mugs of orangeade and handed a full mug to Suzie.

"Camping's great, isn't it, Nicky? I don't know why people bother to live in houses. It's much more fun living in a tent."

Nicky sat back to enjoy her drink. Unfortunately, she sat on the switchbox, and within a few minutes brought Mr White at a panting run to the tent.

"What's happened? What's the matter?" he gasped out.

"Sorry, Daddy," Suzie apologised. "Nicky sat on the switchbox by mistake."

"What's she doing sitting anywhere?" demanded Mr White. "She ought to be in bed. Now go to sleep or I'll put you both in the dustbin."

"Sorry, Daddy! Goodnight again!"

Groaning, Mr White stumped away.

"Daddy's right, Nicky," said Suzie. "He won't let us camp out again if we disturb him. We'd better get some shut-eye."

The girls finished their drinks and snuggled down into their sleeping-bags.

They had both had a tiring day in the fresh air, and it wasn't long before they dropped off to sleep; but as it grew darker it grew colder, and the noise of wind in the trees and the rumble of a distant train woke Nicky. For a moment she lay awake staring into the dark. She heard a car in the adjoining road. Then she heard low voices.

"Are you asleep, Suzie?"

"Yes," replied Suzie.

"Oh! Sorry I woke you."

"What d'you want?"

"Would you like some more orangeade? The bottle's still half full."

"Good idea!"

Nicky switched on her torch and fished the bottle out of her sleeping-bag.

"Don't sit on the push-button this time," Suzie warned her, "or you'll have Daddy down here with the dustbin."

"Don't worry." Nicky poured out two mugs of orangeade. "Are you scared at all, Suzie?"

"Scared? What of?"

"Well, spooks. There could be spooks about."

"I don't believe in spooks."

Nicky picked up the torch and put it under her chin so that it cast ugly shadows across her face. She grinned at Suzie, who flicked orangeade at her from her mug.

"Ow!" yelled Nicky.

"Sounds like you're scared!" grinned Suzie. "Why not go outside and walk round the tent? You'll see there's nothing there but wind and trees and garden—not a spook in sight."

Nicky gulped down her drink and snuggled down in her sleeping-bag. "I wouldn't go outside now for—for six packets of biscuits, although I am a bit peckish."

Suzie settled down again. "I'm hungry too. What did you do with those sandwiches we got ready?"

"I ate them."

"Pity! An apple would help to stave off the pangs."

"An apple? Gosh, yes, we could get one from the tree. You come with me and I'll climb up the tree."

Reluctantly, Suzie tumbled out of her sleeping-bag. Nicky crept out of the tent and made her way to the apple-tree. She climbed up and sat on a branch.

"Hoot, hoot!" she called down softly. "I'm a wise old owl, Suzie."

"You look more like a silly young owl," said Suzie. "Hurry up and pick a couple of apples, the biggest you can find."

"Hey, Suzie, there's a car outside the park."

"A car? What's it doing there?" Suzie ran to the hedge and peered through it. A van stood in the road outside the attractive public park that spread opposite their house.

"It's only an old van. Hurry up with those apples, Nicky. It's chilly out here."

"I've got them. Catch!"

Nicky grinned as she pretended to throw down the apples and saw Suzie hold up her hands to catch them. "You're sure to miss, so I'll bring them," she said, and climbed down the tree. "Oh no, I think I've torn my pyjamas."

"Trust you! I say, Nicky, that van—it's a bit suspicious, isn't it? I mean, what's it doing out here at this time of night?"

"Perhaps it's broken down and the owner has left it there."

"He hasn't, you know. Look, Nicky! There are two of them. Keep quiet!"

Nicky gazed across the road as two shadowy figures appeared, vague in the dimness of the park.

Nicky crept out of the tent and made her way to the apple-tree. She climbed up and sat on a branch

They were each carrying something bulky, for the girls could see that their arms were circling something held against their chests.

The figures reached the railings enclosing the park. They stopped and put whatever it was they were carrying through an opening and then crawled through themselves.

Suzie whispered to Nicky: "They're getting through the railings, Nicky. They must have bent the rails to make a way through."

"They're up to something, that's for sure," muttered Nicky. "Wish we could call Dad."

"We mustn't let them hear us. Stay still and keep quiet."

Stealthily, the two figures, who seemed to the watching girls to be youngish, picked up their bulky burdens and crossed to the van. Opening the double doors at the back very quietly, they thrust the objects inside.

"If we don't do something they'll get away, Suzie," Nicky breathed out. "I'm going to run to the tent and ring the alarm for Daddy."

"Don't make a noise or we'll be spotted," said Suzie.

She cast an apprehensive glance at the two men by the van as Nicky hurried away, but the men didn't pause in what they were doing.

Nicky padded swiftly to the tent. The van's engine started up. The second of the two men fastened the van's door and then ran to the front and climbed in. As the van glided away, Suzie had a clear glimpse of the number-plate on the back, and made a mental note of it.

"They've gone," she told Nicky, as she hurried back to the tent.

A few minutes later an irate

Mr White came running down the garden.

"What's up? Don't say you sat on the push-button again. What did you ring for? You woke me out of the depths of sleep."

The girls explained. To their dismay, Mr White snarled.

"You'd no business to be up the apple-tree, especially not in the middle of the night or the small hours of the morning. As for your reason for waking me up, I don't believe a word of it."

"But it's true, Daddy!" declared Suzie earnestly.

Nicky drew her hand in a gruesome gesture across her throat. "Cut my throat if I tell a lie, Daddy."

"Don't say such things!" said Mr White sternly. "You rang that alarm by mistake and you've made up this unlikely story to excuse yourselves. Now go back to bed and get some sleep and let me get mine."

He glared at the twins, gave another growl, and stumped off back to the house, muttering dark threats.

"That's parents for you!" said Nicky bitterly. "They never believe you."

"Daddy's always cross when he gets woken up," mused Suzie. "He goes on as if someone's committed a crime if you happen to wake him out of his nap after

"Don't make a noise or we'll be spotted," said Suzie

dinner on Sunday. I just don't understand it at all."

"Anyway, we know what we saw even if nobody believes us," said Nicky.

Both girls were now so tired that they dropped off to sleep almost as soon as they were in their sleeping-bags. They didn't wake again until morning. Then they went into the house for breakfast. Mr White grunted a greeting. He'd lost a lot of sleep and wasn't feeling a lot of parental affection for his twins at the moment. Mrs White smiled at them, asked whether they'd slept well, and brought them their cornflakes.

They were eating their third bowl of cornflakes when the front-door bell rang. Mrs White answered it. When she came back in the room her face was pale.

"What's the matter?" asked Mr White.

"That was Mrs Dewer. She says it's the park this time. Thieves got through the railings and took away scores and scores of plants—dug them up. The plants are worth hundreds of pounds, Mrs Dewer says. And to think our girls were camping out not a stone's throw away from where it was happening! Oh, George, I knew we should never have let them sleep out alone! Anything could have happened to them. I'll never let them camp out again—not until those thieves are caught. I'm sure they must be the same ones who broke into the Guide hall."

Very slowly Mr White put his knife and fork down. Then he scratched his head. Then he rubbed his chin and cleared his throat.

"Our girls—h'm—heard—er—saw a van parked outside the park last night—late last night. They—er—told me, but I—er—I'm afraid I didn't believe them. I thought they were—well, hoaxing me. I thought they'd rung the alarm in error. I was —well—er—wrong, it seems." He turned to Suzie and Nicky. "I think your van must have been the one used to take away the stolen plants. I'm sorry I disbelieved you. It's a thousand pities I didn't accept what you said, as it would have made it much easier for the police to track them down at that time of night if I'd phoned them."

"I got the van's number," said Suzie. "That should help."

"You got the van's number!" cried Mr White. "My dear girl, that's wonderful."

"Yes," said Suzie. "It was SNL 47M."

"Are you sure?" asked Mr White. "I will phone the police at once. You are quite sure of the number?"

"Oh, yes. It's easy to remember if you link the letters with other words. S and N stand for Suzie and Nicky; 47 is the number of the house next door Aunt Maureen's in Edinburgh, and M is easy to remember."

"We learn to be observant at Guides," Nicky put in with a grin.

It's easy to remember if you link the letters with other words

Mr White was beaming. He hurried out to telephone the police. "When you've finished breakfast," he called over his shoulder, "I want you to pack up your tent. I'd like the garden to be left as tidy as it was before."

Suzie and Nicky looked at each other and grimaced. After breakfast they went into the garden and to their tent.

"I enjoyed camping out last night," said Nicky. "It's a pity we can't do it again tonight, but I'm afraid we won't be allowed."

"We'll have to wait a whole year before we can camp with the Company," grumbled Suzie.

Halfway through the morning a police car pulled up outside the house. Two policemen came into the garden with Mr and Mrs White.

"Are these the two girls?" asked the police-sergeant.

Mr White nodded.

"I haven't done anything," said Nicky—"at least, I don't think so."

"I'm innocent too," said Suzie.

The police sergeant laughed. "We came to thank you for leading us to the burglars who have been plaguing us for the last few months. We tracked down their van, thanks to you, and when we searched their premises we discovered camping gear and a lot of other stolen property that will put them in prison for a few years!" He shook hands with the two girls. "Now that the Girl Guides will have their camping gear back I suppose you two will go camping with them."

Suzie and Nicky nodded, grinning happily.

"Well, enjoy yourselves! Thanks again for your help."

The policemen went back to their car. Mr and Mrs White waved them off and then returned to the twins.

"Camping with the Company for a whole week!" chortled Suzie. "That'll be great."

Nicky began to unpack the tent.

"What are you doing?" asked Mr White.

"Mum said she wouldn't let us camp out again until the thieves were caught," explained Nicky. "Well, they have been caught, so we can camp out in the garden again tonight, eh, Mum?"

Mr and Mrs White looked at each other, but neither said a word. ●

Answers to Puzzles and Quiz

Just the Job (p.59)

1. You're obviously happiest out of doors, and we wouldn't mind betting that you love animals! Why not combine the two by becoming a KENNEL MAID?

2. You have a very caring, capable nature. Becoming a NURSE could satisfy your urge to look after people, and be a very rewarding career for you.

3. You would make a perfect NANNY! Other people can't bear children screaming – you love them, the more the merrier!

4. You are interested in looking after yourself, and with your ability to study things deeply and closely, you would make a good DENTIST.

5. Always doodling, passionately interested in new clothes – put them together and what have you got? A FASHION DESIGNER – that's the one for you!

6. You have your head in the clouds, career wise. But one thing you know for certain – you could never be happy in a routine nine-to-five job. So what about becoming an AIR HOSTESS?

7. You would love a glamorous job, but are willing to work hard to get there. There's one job which involves a lot of both – a MODEL. Could be you?

8. You have so much creative talent, it would be a shame to waste it. You would probably do very well as an ACTRESS, provided you remember that actresses all too frequently spend as much time 'resting' as acting!

9. Your no-nonsense approach to money will take you all the way to the bank – as a BANK MANAGER. Of course, everyone has to start at the bottom – but we're sure you will soon be at the top.

10. You could talk your way out of anything! But you do know what you are talking about most of the time, which is one reason why you would make an excellent LAWYER.

11. You always seem to be the one who knows everyone else's secrets – and passes them on! But don't despair – there's a place for you as a JOURNALIST – the more 'secrets' you uncover, the happier your editor will be!

12. You have a very strong sense of what is fair and correct. 'Let justice be done' could be your motto. You would be a first rate POLICEWOMAN.

13. You have a neat and orderly mind and don't mind doing things for others. You probably enjoy shorthand and typing, and would make someone an excellent SECRETARY.

14. You're probably the one who *always* has her nose in a book, wherever you are! But a love of books is a very good thing – and being a LIBRARIAN would be a very good thing for you!

15. You're very much a girl of the eighties – you know where you're going and always make plans well in advance. Computers are going to be the big advancement of the decade – and you could be advancing with them as a COMPUTER OPERATOR.

16. Really, if you've answered all the questions truthfully, then there's only one job suitable for someone as solitary as you – a LIGHTHOUSE KEEPER!

Guides' Contributions (p.62)

Answers: Agility, Angler, Aquarist, Artist, Athlete, Boatswain, Camper, Challenge, Collector, Cook, Craft, Cyclist, Dancer, Farmer, Folksinger, Health, Heritage, Hiker, Horsewoman, Hostess, Knitter, Laundress, Reader, Skater, Skier, Traveller, World Friendship, Writer.

Camping Crossword (p.67)

1. Map,
2. Primus,
3. Sheath,
4. Haft,
5. Tinder,
6. Rightangles,
7. Sandvic,
8. Compass,
9. Simmering
10. Green,
11. Nightshade,
12. Elder,
13. Rucsac,
14. Clear,
15. Rust,
16. Thanks,
17. Striking,
18. Gipsy

Campsite Problem (p. 67)

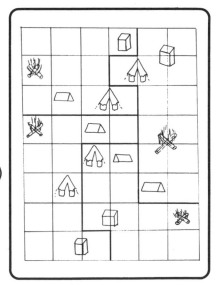

Fascinating

Photos